CELTIC WARRIORS AND GIANTS

CELTIC WARRIORS AND GIANTS

EDITED BY
JAMES STEVENSON

This edition published in 2024 by Arcturus Publishing Limited
26/27 Bickels Yard, 151–153 Bermondsey Street,
London SE1 3HA

Copyright © Arcturus Holdings Limited

All rights reserved. No part of this publication may be reproduced, stored in a retrieval system, or transmitted, in any form or by any means, electronic, mechanical, photocopying, recording or otherwise, without prior written permission in accordance with the provisions of the Copyright Act 1956 (as amended). Any person or persons who do any unauthorised act in relation to this publication may be liable to criminal prosecution and civil claims for damages.

AD012433UK

Printed in China

CONTENTS

INTRODUCTION 7

THE COMING OF CUCULAIN
PREFACE 11
I THE RED BRANCH 13
II THE BOYS OF THE ULTONIANS 19
III DETHCAEN'S NURSLING 23
IV SETANTA RUNS AWAY 27
V THE NEW BOY 35
VI THE SMITH'S SUPPER PARTY 41
VII SETANTA AND THE SMITH'S DOG 45
VIII SETANTA, THE PEACE-MAKER 49
IX THE CHAMPION AND THE KING 55
X DEIRDRÉ 59
XI THERE WAS WAR IN ULSTER 71
XII THE SACRED CHARIOT 75
XIII THE WEIRD HORSES 79
XIV THE KNIGHTING OF CUCULAIN 85
XV ACROSS THE MEARINGS AND AWAY 99
XVI THE RETURN OF CUCULAIN 111
BALOR ON TORY ISLAND 117
BALOR OF THE EVIL EYE AND LUI LAVADA HIS
GRANDSON 125
FIN MACCOOL AND THE DAUGHTER OF
THE KING OF THE WHITE NATION 135
FIN MACCOOL, THE THREE GIANTS, AND THE
SMALL MEN 153
FIN MACCOOL, CEADACH OG, AND THE FISH-HAG 167
FIN MACCOOL, FAOLAN, AND THE MOUNTAIN
OF HAPPINESS 179
FIN MACCOOL, THE HARD GILLA, AND THE HIGH
KING 197
THE BATTLE OF VENTRY 207
NOTES 217

INTRODUCTION

This collection showcases a selection of facinating tales about some of Ireland's greatest warriors and giants: Cuculain, Finn MacCool and Balor. The first half of this book includes Standish O'Grady's volume *The Coming of Cuculain* which is followed by a seclection of Jeremiah Curtin's short stories on Finn MacCool and Balor.

Standish O'Grady was born in 1846 in Castletownbere, Ireland, to the Reverend Thomas O'Grady and Susanna Dowe. Thomas, a rector of the Church of Ireland, encouraged the family's evangelical beliefs, and O'Grady inherited his father's fascination with supernatural forces.

In 1856, O'Grady began studying at Tipperary Grammar School and would later receive a scholarship to Trinity College, Dublin. He thrived in his studies of ethics, debate and philosophy and went on to practise law. However, O'Grady put little time into his legal practice and instead supplemented his income as a political writer for various Irish papers. In 1878 and 1880, respectively, O'Grady published two volumes on Irish history, drawing the attention and respect of William Butler Yeats. Some of his more prominent works included *The Coming of Cuculain* (1894) and *The Chain of Gold* (1895).

Included here, *The Coming of Cuculain* is a retelling of the titular Gaelic hero's adventures. The subject of fascination throughout centuries of folklore, the demi-god Cuculain has long been a pillar of justice and courage in Ireland. Countless stories tell of Cuculain's legendary exploits but few tell of his rise to greatness quite like *The Coming*. The novel follows young Setanta, a virtuous warrior learning to control his superhuman strength and, ultimately, earn his true name. O'Grady's rich and vibrant retelling of Cuculain's origin solidifies the hero as both an epic figure and a symbol of bravery.

O'Grady remained in Ireland until 1918 when he left to settle with his eldest son on the Isle of Wight. He died unexpectedly in 1928, leaving behind an extensive body of work, having forever changed the trajectory of Irish literature. Yeats referred to O'Grady as the 'Father of the Celtic Revival'.

Also included in this captivating collection are a number of Irish legends retold by Jeremiah Curtin. Curtin was born in 1835 in Detroit, Michigan, to David Curtin and Ellen Furlong. Both David and Ellen were farmers and relocated the family to a farm in Greenfield, Milwaukee, an Irish immigrant community in Wisconsin.

In 1858, Curtin enrolled in Carroll College while also working on the family farm. In the autumn of 1859, Curtin left home to study at Phillips Exeter Academy in New Hampshire and eventually enrolled at Harvard in 1862. Obtaining a Bachelor of Arts degree, he crossed paths with students such as Francis James Child, who shared his interest in folklore. After graduating in 1863, Curtin practised law in New York before moving to Russia to serve as a secretary to Cassius M. Clay in 1864. In 1868, Curtin returned to Milwaukee to study languages and later married Alma Cardell who would serve as his travel partner and collaborator.

In 1883, the Curtins moved to Washington DC, where Curtin worked for the Bureau of American Ethnology. During this era of his life, he travelled to Ireland several times, fascinated with the connection between language and folklore. These voyages spurred him to write *Myths and Folklore of Ireland* in 1889. Extremely well received, the book resulted in a deal with Charles Dana, the editor of the *New York Sun*. This enabled Curtin to travel again to Ireland and collect legends from native speakers. The result of these trips was Curtin's body of work including *Hero-Tales of Ireland* (1894).

Taken from *Hero-Tales of Ireland*, Curtin's stories in this collection follow the gripping adventures of Ireland's fearsome giants Fin MacCool and Balor.

He returned to Ireland for the last time in 1899 and collected a number of tales that would be published after his death in 1906.

THE COMING OF CUCULAIN

Standish O'Grady

PREFACE

There are three great cycles of Gaelic literature. The first treats of the gods; the second of the Red Branch Knights of Ulster and their contemporaries; the third is the so-called Ossianic. Of the Ossianic, Finn is the chief character; of the Red Branch cycle, Cuculain, the hero of our tale.

Cuculain and his friends are historical characters, seen as it were through mists of love and wonder, whom men could not forget, but for centuries continued to celebrate in countless songs and stories. They were not literary phantoms, but actual existences; imaginary and fictitious characters, mere creatures of idle fancy, do not live and flourish so in the world's memory. And as to the gigantic stature and superhuman prowess and achievements of those antique heroes, it must not be forgotten that all art magnifies, as if in obedience to some strong law; and so, even in our own times, Grattan, where he stands in artistic bronze, is twice as great as the real Grattan thundering in the Senate. I will therefore ask the reader, remembering the large manner of the antique literature from which our tale is drawn, to forget for a while that there is such a thing as scientific history, to give his imagination a holiday, and follow with kindly interest the singular story of the boyhood of Cuculain, 'battle-prop of the valour and torch of the chivalry of the Ultonians'.

I have endeavoured so to tell the story as to give a general idea of the cycle, and of primitive heroic Irish life as reflected in that literature, laying the cycle, so far as accessible, under contribution to furnish forth the tale. Within a short compass I would bring before swift modern readers the more striking aspects of a literature so vast and archaic as to repel all but students.

I

THE RED BRANCH

'THERE WERE GIANTS IN THE EARTH IN THOSE DAYS, THE SAME WERE MIGHTY MEN WHICH WERE OF YORE MEN OF RENOWN.'

The Red Branch feasted one night in their great hall at Emain Macha. So vast was the hall that a man, such as men are now, standing in the centre and shouting his loudest, would not be heard at the circumference, yet the low laughter of the King sitting at one end was clearly audible to those who sat around the Champion at the other. The sons of Dithorba made it, giants of the elder time, labouring there under the brazen shoutings of Macha and the roar of her sounding thongs. Its length was a mile and nine furlongs and a cubit. With her brooch pin she ploughed its outline upon the plain, and its breadth was not much less. Trees such as the earth nourished then upheld the massy roof beneath which feasted that heroic brood, the great-hearted children of Rury, huge offspring of the gods and giants of the dawn of time. For mighty exceedingly were these men. At the noise of them running to battle all Ireland shook, and the illimitable Lir[1] trembled in his watery halls; the roar of their brazen chariots reverberated from the solid canopy of heaven, and their war-steeds drank rivers dry.

A vast murmur rose from the assembly, for like distant thunder or the far-off murmuring of agitated waters was the continuous hum of their blended conversation and laughter, while, ever and anon, cleaving the many-tongued confusion, uprose friendly voices, clearer and stronger than battle-trumpets, when one hero challenged another to drink, wishing him victory and success, and his words rang round the hollow dome. Innumerable candles, tall as spears, illuminated the scene. The eyes of the heroes sparkled, and their faces, white and ruddy, beamed with festal mirth and mutual affection. Their yellow hair shone. Their banqueting attire, white and scarlet, glowed against the outer gloom. Their round brooches and mantle-pins of gold, or silver, or golden bronze, their drinking vessels and instruments of festivity, flashed and glittered in the light. They rejoiced in their glory and their might, and in the inviolable amity in which they were knit together, a host of comrades, a knot of heroic valour and affection which no strength or cunning, and no power, seen or unseen, could ever relax or untie.

At one extremity of the vast hall, upon a raised seat, sat their young king, Concobar Mac Nessa, slender, handsome, and upright. A canopy of bronze, round as the bent sling of the Sun-god, the long-handed, far-shooting son of Ethlend,[2] encircled his head. At his right hand lay a staff of silver. Far away at the other end of the hall, on a raised seat, sat the Champion Fergus Mac Roy, like a colossus. The stars and clouds of night were round his head and shoulders seen through the wide and high entrance of the dun, whose doors no man had ever seen closed and barred. Aloft, suspended from the dim rafters, hung the naked forms of great men clear against the dark dome, having the cords of their slaughter around their necks and their white limbs splashed with blood. Kings were they who had murmured against the sovereignty of the Red Branch. Through the wide doorway out of the night flew a huge bird, black and grey, unseen, and soaring upwards sat upon the rafters, its eyes like burning fire. It was the Mor-Reega,[3] or Great Queen, the far-striding terrible daughter of Iarnmas (Iron-Death). Her voice was like the shouting of ten thousand men. Dear to her were these heroes. More she rejoiced in them feasting than in the battle-prowess of the rest.

When supper was ended their bard, in his singing robes and girt around the temples with a golden fillet, stood up and sang. He sang how once a king of the Ultonians, having plunged into the sea-depths, there slew a monster which had wrought much havoc amongst fishers and seafaring men. The heroes attended to his song, leaning forward with bright eyes. They applauded the song and the singer, and praised the valour of the heroic man[4] who had done that deed. Then the champion struck the table with his clenched hand, and addressed the assembly. Wrath and sorrow were in his voice. It resembled the brool of lions heard afar by seafaring men upon some savage shore on a still night.

'Famous deeds,' he said, 'are not wrought now amongst the Red Branch. I think we are all become women. I grow weary of these huntings in the morning and mimic exercises of war, and this training of steeds and careering of brazen chariots stained never with aught but dust and mire, and these unearned feastings at night and vain applause of the brave deeds of our forefathers. Come now, let us make an end of this. Let us conquer Banba[5] wholly in all her green borders, and let the realms of Lir, which sustain no foot of man, be the limit of our sovereignty. Let us gather the tributes of all Ireland, after many battles and much warlike toil. Then more sweetly shall we drink while the bards chaunt our own prowess. Once I knew a coward who boasted endlessly about his forefathers, and at last my anger rose, and with a flat hand I slew him in the middle of his speech, and paid no eric, for he was nothing. We have the blood of heroes in our veins, and we sit here nightly boasting about them; about Rury, whose name we bear, being all his children; and Macha the warrioress, who brought hither bound the sons of Dithorba and made them rear this mighty dun; and Combat son of Fiontann; and my namesake Fergus,[6] whose crooked mouth was no dishonour, and the rest of our hero sires; and we consume the rents and tributes of Ulster which they by their prowess conquered to us, and which flow hither in abundance from every corner of the province. Valiant men, too, will one day come hither and slay us as I slew that boaster, and here in Emain Macha their bards will praise them. Then in the halls of the dead shall we say to our sires, "All that you got for us by your blood and your sweat that have we lost, and the glory of the Red Branch is at an end."'

That speech was pleasing to the Red Branch, and they cried out that Fergus Mac Roy had spoken well. Then all at once, on a sudden impulse, they sang the battle-song of the Ultonians, and shouted for the war so that the building quaked and rocked, and in the hall of the weapons there was a clangour of falling shields, and men died that night for extreme dread, so mightily shouted the Ultonians around their king and around Fergus. When the echoes and reverberations of that shout ceased to sound in the vaulted roof and in the far recesses and galleries, then there arose somewhere upon the night a clear chorus of treble voices, singing, too, the war-chant of the Ultonians, as when rising out of the clangour of brazen instruments of music there shrills forth the clear sound of fifes. For the immature scions of the Red Branch, boys and tender youths, awakened out of slumber, heard them, and from remote dormitories responded to their sires, and they cried aloud together and shouted. The trees of Ulster shed their early leaves and buds at that shout, and birds fell dead from the branches.

Concobar struck the brazen canopy with his silver rod. The smitten brass rang like a bell, and the Ultonians in silence hearkened for the words of their clear-voiced king.

'No ruler of men,' he said, 'however masterful and imperious, could withstand this torrent of martial ardour which rolls to-night through the souls of the children of Rury, still less I, newly come to this high throne, having been but as it were yesterday your comrade and equal, till Fergus, to my grief, resigned the sovereignty, and caused me, a boy, to be made king of Ulla and captain of the Red Branch. But now I say, ere we consider what province or territory shall first see the embattled Red Branch cross her borders, let us enquire of Cathvah the Ard-Druid[7], whether the omens be propitious, and whether through his art he is able to reveal to us some rite to be performed or prohibition to be observed.'

That proposal was not pleasing to Fergus, but it pleased the Red Branch, and they praised the wisdom of their king.

Then Cathvah the Ard-Druid spake.

'It hath been foretold,' he said, 'long since, that the Ultonians shall win glory such as never was and never will be, and that their fame shall endure till the world's end. But, first, there are prophecies to be accomplished and predictions to be fulfilled. For ere these things may be there shall come a child to Emain Macha, attended by clear portents from the gods; through him shall arise our deathless fame. Also it hath been foretold that there shall be great divisions and fratricidal strife amongst the children of Rury, a storm of war which shall strip the Red Branch nigh bare.'

Fergus was wroth at this, and spoke words of scorn concerning the diviner, and concerning all omens, prohibitions, and prophecies. Concobar, too, and all the Red Branch, rebuked the prophet. Yet he stood against them like a rock warred on by winds which stand immovable, let them rage as they will, and refused to take back his words. Then said Concobar:

'Many are the prophecies which came wandering down upon the mouths of men, but they are not all to be trusted alike. Of those which have passed thy lips, O Cathvah, we utterly reject the last, and think the less of thee for having reported it. But the former which concerns the child of promise hath been ever held a sure prophecy, and as such passed down through all the diviners from the time of Amargin, the son of Milesius, who first prophesied for the Gael. And now being arch-king of the Ultonians, I command thee to divine for us when the coming of the child shall be.'

Then Cathvah, the Ard-Druid, put on his divining apparel and took his divining instruments in his hands, and made his symbols of power upon the air. And at first he was silent, and, being in a trance, stared out before him with wide eyes full of wonder and amazement, directing his gaze to the east. In the end he cried out with a loud voice, and prophesying, sang this lay:

'Yea, he is coming. He draweth nigh.
Verily it is he whom I behold –
The predicted one – the child of many prophecies –
Chief flower of the Branch that is over all –
The mainstay of Emaiti Macha – the battle-prop of the Ultonians –
The torch of the valour and chivalry of the North –
The star that is to shine for ever upon the forehead of the Gael.
It is he who slumbers upon Slieve Fuad –
The child who is like a star –
Like a star upon Slieve Fuad.

There is a light around him never kindled at the hearth of Lu,
The Grey of Macha keeps watch and ward for him,[8]
And the whole mountain is filled with the Tuatha de Danan.'[9]

Then his vision passed from the Druid, he raised up his long white hands and gave thanks to the high gods of Erin that he had lived to see this day.

When Cathvah had made an end of speaking there was a great silence in the hall.

II

THE BOYS OF THE ULTONIANS

'And dear the school-boy spot
We ne'er forget though there we are forgot.'

BYRON.

'There were his young barbarians all at play.'

BYRON.

In the morning Fergus Mac Roy said to the young king, 'What shall we do this day, O Concobar? Shall we lead forth our sweet-voiced hounds into the woods and rouse the wild boar from his lair, and chase the swift deer, or shall we drive afar in our chariots and visit one of our subject kings and take his tribute as hospitality, which, according to thee, wise youth, is the best, for it is agreeable to ourselves and not displeasing to the man that is tributary?

'Nay,' said Concobar, 'let us wait and watch this day. Hast thou forgotten the words of Cathvah?'

'Truly, in a manner I had,' said Fergus, 'for I never much regarded, the race of seers, or deemed the birds more than pleasant songsters, and the stars as a fair spectacle, or druidic instruments aught but toys.'

'Let us play at chess on the lawn of the dun,' said the king, 'while our boys exercise themselves at hurling on the green.'

'It is agreeable to me,' said Fergus, 'though well thou knowest, dear foster-son, that I am not thy match at the game.'

What the champion said was true, for in royal wisdom the king far excelled his foster-father, and that was the reason why Fergus had abdicated the supreme captaincy of the Red Branch in favour of

Concobar, for though his heart was great his understanding was not fine and acute like the understanding of his foster-son.

The table was set for them upon the lawn before the great painted and glowing palace, and three-footed stools were put on either side of that table, and bright cloths flung over them. A knight to whom that was a duty brought forth and unfolded a chess-board of ivory on which silver squares alternated with gold, cunningly wrought by some ancient cerd,[10] a chief jewel of the realm; another bore in his hand the man-bag, also a wonder, glistening, made of netted wires of findruiney,[11] and took therefrom the men and disposed them in their respective places on the board, each in the centre of his own square. The gold men were on the squares of silver, and the silver on the squares of gold. The table was set under the shadowing branches of a great tree, for it was early summer and the sun shone in his strength. So Concobar and Fergus, lightly laughing, affectionate and mirthful, the challenger and the challenged, came forth through the wide doorway of the dun. Armed youths went with them. The right arm of Fergus was cast lightly over the shoulder of Concobar, and his ear was inclined to him as the young king talked, for their mutual affection was very great and like that of a great boy and a small boy when such, as often happens, become attached to one another. So Concobar and Fergus sat down to play, though right seldom did the Champion win any game from the King.

Concobar beckoned to him one of the young knights. It was Conall Carna,[12] son of Amargin, youngest of the knights of Concobar. 'Son of Amargin,' said the king, 'do thou watch over the boys this day in their pastimes. See that nothing is done unseemly or unjust. Observe narrowly the behaviour and disposition of the lads, and report all things clearly to me on the morrow.'

So saying, he moved one of the pieces on the board, and Conall Carna strode away southwards to where the boys were already dividing themselves into two parties for a match at hurling.

That son of Amargin was the handsomest youth of all the province. White and ruddy was his beardless countenance. Bright as gold which boils over the edge of the refiner's crucible was his hair, which fell curling upon his broad shoulders and over the circumference of his shield, outshining its splendour. By his side hung a short sword with a handle of walrus-tooth; in his left hand he bore two spears tipped with glittering bronze. Fergus and Concobar watched him as he strode over the grass; Concobar noted his beauty and grace, but Fergus noted his great strength. Soon the boys, being divided into two equal bands, began their pastime and contended, eagerly urging the ball to and fro. The noise of the stricken ball and the clash of the hurles shod with bronze, the cries of the captains, and the shouting of the boys, filled all the air.

That good knight stood midway between the goals, eastward from the players. Ever and anon with a loud clear voice he reproved the youths, and they hearkening took his rebukes in silence and obeyed his words. Cathvah came forth that day upon the lawn, and thus spoke one of the boys to another in some pause of the game, 'Yonder, see! the Ard-Druid of the Province. Wherefore comes he forth from his druidic chambers to-day at this hour, such not being his wont?' And the other answered lightly, laughing, and with boyish heedlessness, 'I know not wherefore; but well he knows himself.' And therewith ran to meet the ball which passed that way. There was yet a third who watched the boys. He stood afar off on the edge of the plain. He had a little shield strapped on his back, two javelins in one hand, and a hurle in the other. He was very young and fair. He stood looking fixedly at the hurlers, and as he looked he wept. It was the child who had been promised to the Ultonians.

III

DETHCAEN'S NURSLING

'Very small and beautiful like a star.' HOMER.

'I love all that thou lovest,
Spirit of delight;
The fresh earth in new leaves drest,
And the blessed night;
Starry evening and the morn,
When the golden mists are born.'

SHELLEY.

Sualtam of Dun Dalgan on the Eastern Sea, took to wife Dectera, daughter of Factna the Righteous. She was sister of Concobar Mac Nessa. Sualtam was the King of Cooalney[13] a land of woods and mountains, an unproductive headland reaching out into the Ictian Sea.

Dectera bare a son to Sualtam, and they called him Setanta. That was his first name. His nurse was Dethcaen, the druidess, daughter of Cathvah the druid, the mighty wizard and prophet of the Crave Rue. His breast-plate[14] of power, woven of druidic verse, was upon Ulla[15] in his time, upon all the children of Rury in their going out and their coming in, in war and in peace. Dethcaen[16] sang her own songs of protection for the child. His mother gave the child suck, but the rosy-cheeked, beautiful, sweetly-speaking daughter of Cathvah nursed him. On her breast and knee she bare him with great love. Light of foot and slender was Dethcaen; through the wide dun of Sualtam she went with her nursling, singing songs. She it was that discovered his first ges,[17] namely, that no one should awake him while he slept. He had others, sacred prohibitions which it was unlawful to transgress, but this was discovered by Dethcaen. She discovered it while he was yet a babe. With her own hands Dethcaen washed his garments and bathed his tiny limbs; lightly and cheerfully she sprang from her couch at night when she heard his voice, and raised him from the cradle and wrapped him tenderly, and put him into the hands of his mother. She watched him when he slumbered; there was great stillness in the palace of Sualtam when the child slept. She repeated for him many tales and taught him nothing base. When he was three years old, men came with hounds to hunt the stream which ran past Dun Dalgan.[18] Early in the morning Setanta heard the baying of the hounds and the shouting of the men. They were hunting a great water-dog which had his abode in this stream. Setanta leaped from his couch and ran to the river. Well he knew that stream and all its pools and shallows; he knew where the water-dog had his den. Thither by circuit he ran and stood before the month of the same, having a stone in either hand. The hunted water-dog drew nigh. Maddened with fear and rage he gnashed his teeth and growled, and then charged at the child. There, O Setanta, with the stroke of one stone thou didst slay the water-dog! The dog was carried in procession with songs to the dun of Sualtam, who that night gave a great feast and called many to rejoice with him, because his only son had done bravely. A prophet who was there said, 'Thou shalt do many feats in thy time, O Setanta, and the last will resemble the first.'

Setanta played along the sand and by the frothing waves of the sea-shore under the dun. He had a ball and an ashen hurle shod with bronze; joyfully he used to drive his ball along the hard sand, shouting among his small playmates. The captain of the guard gave him a sheaf of toy javelins and taught him how to cast, and made for him a sword of lath and a painted shield. They made for him a high chair. In the great hall of the dun, when supper was served, he used to sit beside the champion of that small realm, at the south end of the table over against the king. Ever as evening drew on and the candles were lit, and the instruments of festivity and the armour and trophies on the walls and pillars shone in the cheerful light, and the people of Sualtam sat down

DETHCAEN'S NURSLING

rejoicing, there too duly appeared Setanta over against his father by the side of the champion, very fair and pure, yellow-haired, in his scarlet bratta fastened with a little brooch of silver, serene and grave beyond his years, shining there like a very bright star on the edge of a thunder-cloud, so that men often smiled to see them together.

While Sualtam and his people feasted, the harper harped and trained singers sang. Every day the floor was strewn with fresh rushes or dried moss or leaves. Every night at a certain hour the bed-makers went round spreading couches for the people of Sualtam. Sometimes the king slept with his people in the great hall. Then one warrior sat awake through the night at his pillow having his sword drawn, and another warrior sat at his feet having his sword drawn. The fire-place was in the midst of the hall. In winter a slave appointed for that purpose from time to time during the night laid on fresh logs. Rude plenty never failed in the dun of Sualtam. In such wise were royal households ordered in the age of the heroes. For the palace, it was of timber staunched with clay and was roofed with rushes. Without it was white with lime, conspicuous afar to mariners sailing in the Muirnict.[19] There was a rampart round the dun and a moat spanned by a drawbridge. Before it there was a spacious lawn. Down that lawn there ever ran a stream of sparkling water. Setanta sailed his boats in the stream and taught it here to be silent, and there to hum in rapids, or to apparel itself in silver and sing liquid notes, or to blow its little trumpet from small cataracts.

IV

SETANTA RUNS AWAY

'For a boy's way is the wind's way.' LONGFELLOW

And now the daily life of that remote dun no longer pleased the boy, for the war-spirit within drave him on. Moreover he longed for comrades and playfellows, for his fearful mother permitted him no longer to associate with children of that rude realm whose conversation and behaviour she misliked for her child. She loved him greatly and perceived not how he changed, or how the new years in their coming and their going both gave and took away continually.

In summer the boy sat often with the chief bard under the thatched eaves of the dun, while the crying swallows above came and went, asking many questions concerning his forefathers back the ascending line up to Rury, and again downwards through the ramifications of that mighty stem, and concerning famous marches and forays, and battles and single combats, and who was worthy and lived and died well, and who not. More than all else he delighted to hear about Fergus Mac Roy, who seemed to him the greatest and best of all the Red Branch. In winter, cradled in strong arms, he listened to the reminiscences and conversation of the men of war as they sat and talked round the blazing logs in the hall, while the light flickered upon warlike faces, and those who drew drink went round bearing mead and ale.

Upon his seventh birthday early in the morning he ran to his mother and cried, 'Mother, send me now to Emain Macha, to my uncle.'

Dectera grew pale when she heard that word and her knees smote together with loving fear. For answer she withdrew him from the society of the men and kept him by herself in the women's quarter, which was called grianan. The grianan was in the north end of the palace behind the king's throne. In the hall men could see above them the rafters which upheld the roof and the joining of the great central pillar with the same. From the upper storey of the grianan a door opened upon the great hall directly above the throne of the king, and before that door was a railed gallery.

Thence it was the custom of Dectera to supervise in the morning the labours of the household thralls and at night to rebuke unseemly revelry, and at the fit hour to command silence and sleep. Thence too in the evening, ere he went to his small couch, Setanta would cry out 'good-night' and 'good slumber' to his friends in the hall, who laughed much amongst themselves for the secret of his immurement was not hid. Moreover, Dectera gave straight commandment to her women, at peril of her displeasure and of sore bodily chastisement, that they should not speak to him any word concerning Emain Macha. The boy as yet knew not where lay the wondrous city, whether in heaven or on earth or beyond the sea. To him it was still as it were a fairy city or in the land of dreams.

One day he saw afar upon the plain long lines of lowing kine and of laden garrans wending north-westward. He questioned his mother concerning that sight. She answered, 'It is the high King's tribute out of Murthemney.'[20]

'Mother,' he said, 'how runs the road hence to the great city?'

'That thou shalt not know,' said his mother, looking narrowly on the boy.

But still the strong spirit from within, irresistible, urged on the lad. One day while his mother conversed with him, inadvertently she uttered certain words, and he knew that the road to Emain Macha went past the mountain of Slieve Fuad.[21] That night he dreamed of Emain Macha, and he rose up early in the morning and clambered on to the roof of the palace through a window and gazed long upon the mountain. The next night too he dreamed of Emain Macha, and heard voices which were unintelligible, and again the third night he heard the voices and one voice said, 'This our labour is vain, let him alone. He

SETANTA RUNS AWAY

is some changeling and not of the blood of Rury. He will be a grazier, I think, and buy cattle and sell them for a profit.' And the other said, 'Nay, let us not leave him yet. Remember how valiantly he faced the fierce water-dog and slew him at one cast.' When he climbed to the roof, as his manner was, to gaze at the mountain, he thought that Slieve Fuad nodded to him and beckoned. He broke fast with his mother and the women that day and ate and drank silently with bright eyes, and when that meal was ended he donned his best attire and took his toy weapons and a new ball and his ashen hurle shod with red bronze.

'Wherefore this holiday attire?' said his mother.

'Because I shall see great people ere I put it off,' he answered.

She kissed him and he went forth as at other times to play upon the lawn by himself. The king sat upon a stone seat hard by the door of the grianan. Under the eaves he sat sunning himself and gazing upon the sea. The boy kneeled and kissed his hand. His father stroked his head and said, 'Win victory and blessings, dear Setanta.' He looked at the lad as if he would speak further, but restrained himself and leaned back again in his seat.

Dectera sat in the window of the upper chamber amongst her women. They sat around her sewing and embroidering. She herself was embroidering a new mantle for the boy against his next birthday, though that indeed was far away, but ever while her hands wrought her eyes were on the lawn.

'Mother,' cried Setanta, 'watch this stroke.'

He flung his ball into the air and as it fell met it with his hurle, leaning back and putting his whole force into the blow, and struck it into the clouds. It was long before the ball fell. It fell at his feet.

'Mother,' he cried again, 'watch this stroke.'

He went to the east mearing of the spacious lawn and struck the ball to the west. It traversed the great lawn ere it touched the earth and bounded shining above the trees. Truly it was a marvellous stroke for one so young. As he went for his ball the boy stood still before the window. 'Give me thy blessing, dear mother,' he said.

'Win victory and blessing for ever, O Setanta,' she answered. 'Truly thou art an expert hurler.'

'These feats,' he replied, 'are nothing to what I shall yet do in needlework, O mother, when I am of age to be trusted with my first needle, and knighted by thy hands, and enrolled amongst the valiant company of thy sewing-women.'

'What meaneth the boy?' said his mother, for she perceived that he spoke awry.

'That his childhood is over, O Dectera,' answered one of her women, 'and that thou art living in the past and in dreams. For who can hold back Time in his career?'

The queen's heart leaped when she heard that word, and the blood forsook her face. She bent down her head over her work and her tears fell. After a space she looked out again upon the lawn to see if the boy had returned, but he had not.

She bade her women go and fetch him, and afterwards the whole household. They called aloud, 'Setanta, Setanta,' but there was no answer, only silence and the watching and mocking trees and a sound like low laughter in the leaves; for Setanta was far away.

The boy came out of that forest on the west side. Soon he struck the great road which from Ath-a-clia[22] ran through Murthemney to Emain Macha, and saw before him the purple mountain of Slieve Fuad. In his left hand was his sheaf of toy javelins; in his right the hurle; his little shield was strapped upon his back. The boy went swiftly, for there was power upon him that day, and with his ashen hurle shod with red bronze ever urged his ball forward. So he went driving, his ball before him. At other times he would cast a javelin far out westward and pursue its flight. Ever as he went there ever flew beside him a grey-necked crow. 'It is a good omen,' said the boy, for he knew that the bird was sacred to the Mor-Reega.

He was amazed at his own speed and the elasticity of his limbs. Once when he rose after having gathered his thrown javelin, a man stood beside him who had the port and countenance of some ancient hero, and whose attire was strange. He was taller and nobler than any living man. He bore a rod-sling in his right hand, and in his left, in a leash of bronze, he led a hound. The hound was like white fire. Setanta could hardly look in that man's face, but he did. The man smiled and said –

'Whither away, my son?'

'To Emain Macha, to my uncle Concobar,' said the boy.

'Dost thou know me, Setanta?' said the man.

'I think thou art Lu Lam-fada Mac Ethlend,'[23] answered Setanta.

'I am thy friend,' said the man, 'fear nothing, for I shall be with thee always.'

Then the man and the hound disappeared as if they had been resolved into the rays of the sun; Setanta saw nothing, only the grey-necked crow starting for flight. Then a second man in a wide blue mantle specked with white like flying foam came against him and flung his mantle over Setanta. There was a sound in his ears like the roaring of the sea.[24] Chariots and horses came from the east after that. Setanta recognised those who urged on the steeds, they were his own people. 'Surely,' he said, 'I shall be taken now.' The men drave past him. 'If I mistake not,' he said, 'the man who flung his mantle over me was Mananan the son of Lir.'

Divers persons, noble and ignoble, passed him on the way, some riding in chariots, some going on foot. They went as though they saw him not.

In the evening he came to Slieve Fuad. He gathered a bed of dried moss and heaped moss upon his shield for a pillow. He wrapped himself in his mantle, and lay down to sleep, and felt neither cold nor hunger. While he slept a great steed, a stallion, grey to whiteness, came close to him, and walked all round him, and smelt him, and stayed by him till the morning.

Setanta was awaked by the loud singing of the birds. Light of heart the boy started from his mossy couch and wondered at that tuneful chorus. The dawning day trembled through the trees still half-bare, for it was the month of May.

'Horses have been here in the night,' said the boy, 'one horse. What mighty hoof marks!' He wondered the more seeing how the marks encircled him. 'I too will one day have a chariot and horses, and a deft charioteer.' He stood musing, 'Is it the grey of Macha?[25] They say that he haunts this mountain.' He hastened to the brook, and finding a deep pool, bathed in the clear pure water and dried himself in his woollen bratta[26] of divers colours. Very happy and joyous was Setanta that day. And he spread out the bratta to dry, and put on his shirt of fine linen and his woollen tunic that reached to the knees in many plaits. Shoes he had none; bare and naked were his swift feet.

'This is the mountain of Fuad the son of Brogan,'[27] said he. 'I would I knew where lies his cairn in this great forest that I might pay my stone-tribute to the hero.' Soon he found it and laid his stone upon the heap. He climbed to the hill's brow and looked westward and saw far away the white shining duns of the marvellous city from which, even now, the morning smoke went up into the windless air. He trembled, and rejoiced, and wept. He stood a long time there gazing at Emain Macha. Descending, he struck again the great road, but he went slowly; he cast not his javelins and drave not his ball. Again, from a rising ground he saw Emain Macha, this time near at hand. He remained there a long time filled with awe and fear. He covered his head with his mantle and wept aloud, and said he would return to Dun Dalgan, that he dared not set unworthy feet in that holy place.

Then he heard the cheerful voices of the boys as they brake from the royal palace and ran down the wide smooth lawn to the hurling-ground. His heart yearned for their companionship, yet he feared greatly, and his mind misgave him as to the manner in which they would receive him. He longed to go to them and say, 'I am little Setanta, and my uncle is the king, and I would be your friend and playfellow.' Hope and love and fear confused his mind. Yet it came to him that he was urged forwards, by whom he knew not. Reluctantly, with many pausings, he drew nigh to the players and stood solitary on the edge of the lawn southwards, for the company that held that barrier were the weaker. He hoped that some one would call to him and welcome him, but none called or welcomed. Silently the child wept, and the front of his mantle was steeped in his tears. Some looked at him, but with looks of cold surprise, as though they said, 'Who is this stranger boy and what doth he here? Would that he took himself away out of this and went elsewhere.' The boy thought that he would be welcomed and made much of because he was a king's son and nephew of the high King of Ulla, and on account of his skill in hurling, and because he himself longed so exceedingly for companions and comrades, and because there were within him such fountains of affection and loving kindness. And many a time happy visions had passed before his eyes awake or asleep of the meeting between himself and his future comrades, but the event itself when it happened was by no means what he had anticipated. For no one kissed him and bade him welcome or took him by the right hand and led him in, and no one seemed glad of his coming and he was here of no account at all. Bitter truly was thy weeping, dear Setanta.

V

THE NEW BOY

> 'I to surrender, to fling away this! So owned by God and Man! so witnessed to! I had rather be rolled into my grave and buried with infamy.'
>
> *Battle-chaunt of a hero of the Saxons*

Once, struck sideways out of the press, the ball bounded into a clear space not far from Setanta. 'Thou of the Javelins,' cried the captain of the distressed party, 'the ball is with thee.' He roared mightily at Setanta. On a sudden Setanta, filled with all the glow and ardour of the mimic battle, cast his javelins to the ground, slipped the strap of his shield over his head, flung the shield beside his javelins on the grass and pursued the bounding ball. He out-ran the rest and took possession of the ball. Now to the right he urged it, now to the left. He played it deftly before every opponent who sought to check his career, and swiftly and cunningly carried it past each of these, and finally with a clear loud stroke sent it straight as a sling-bolt through the middle of the north goal. The boys of his adopted party shouted, and they praised his playing and that final victorious stroke. Setanta went back after that and stood by himself near the south goal. His face was flushed and his eyes sparkled, and he himself trembled with joy, yet was he not in the least exhausted or out of breath.

The captain of the northern company came down with his boys and all the boys who were chief in authority, and they surrounded Setanta and said, 'Thou art here a stranger and on sufferance. We know thee not, but thou art a good hurler and not otherwise, as we think, unmeet to bear us company. Receive now our protection, and we will divide the sides again with a new division and continue the game, for thou art very swift and truly expert in the use of thy hurle.'

The boys regulated all things according to the laws and customs of their elders. And everywhere it was the custom that the weak should accept the protection of the strong and submit themselves to their command. So slaves received masters, so runaways and fugitives got to themselves lords, and sheltered themselves under their protection and paid dues. Setanta's brow fell, and he answered, 'Put not upon me, I pray you, these hard terms. I would be your friend and comrade, I cannot be your subject being what I am.'

And they said, 'Who art thou?'

And he answered, 'I am the son of Dectera of Dun Dalgan, and nephew of the king.'

Then the boy who was captain of the whole school, and the biggest and strongest, stood over him, and said –

'Thou, the king's nephew! the son of Sualtam and Dectera of Dun Dalgan! and comest hither without chariots and horsemen and a prince's retinue and guard. Nay, thou art a churl and a liar to boot, and hie thee hence now with wings at thy heels or verily with sore blows I shall beat thee off the lawn.'

Thereat the blood forsook thy face, O Setanta, O peerless one, and thou stoodest like a still figure carved out of white marble, with the pallor of death in thy immortal face. But that other, indignant to see him stand as one both deaf and dumb, and mistaking his pallor for fear, raised his hurle and struck with all his might at the boy. Setanta sprang back avoiding the blow, and ere the other could recover himself, struck him back-handed over the right ear, whose knees were suddenly relaxed and the useless weapon shaken from his hands. Then some stood aside, but the rest ran upon Setanta to beat him off the lawn and struck at him all together, as well as they could, for their numbers impeded them, and fiercely the stranger defended himself, and many a shrewd stroke he delivered upon his enemies, for the slumbering war-spirit now, for the first time, had awaked in his gentle heart. Many times he was overborne and flung to the ground, but again he arose overthrowing others, never

THE NEW BOY

quitting hold of his hurle, and, whenever he got a free space, grasping that weapon like a war-mace in both hands, he struck down his foes. The skirts of his mantle were torn, only a rag remained round his shoulders, fastened by the brooch; he was covered with blood, his own and his enemies', and his eyes were like burning fire. Then Conall Carna being enraged ran towards the boys, meaning to rebuke their cowardice and with his strong hands hurl them asunder and save the stranger boy. There was not a knight in all Ireland those days who loved battle-fairness better than Conall Carna. Truly he was the pure-burning torch of the chivalry of the Ultonians in his time. But as he ran one withheld him and a voice crying 'Forbear' rang in his ears. Yet he saw no man. He stood still, being astonished, and became aware that this tumult was divinely guided, for as in a trance he saw and heard marvellous things. For the war-steeds of the Ultonians neighed loudly in their stables, and from the Tec Brac, the Speckled House of the Red Branch, rose a clangour of brass, the roar of the shield called Ocean, and the booming of the Gate-of-Battle, and the singing of swords long silent, and the brazen thunder of the revolution of wheels; and he saw strange forms and faces in the air, and the steady sun dancing in the heavens, and a man standing beside the stranger whose face was like the sun. The son of Amargin saw and heard all, for he was a seer and a prophet no less than a warrior. But meantime his battle-fury descended upon Setanta, his countenance was distraught and his strength was multiplied tenfold, and the steam of his war-madness rose above him. He staggered to no blow, but every boy whom he struck fell, and he charged this way and that, and wherever he went they opened before him. Then seeing how they closed in behind him and on each side, he beat his way back to the grassy rampart in which was the goal, and, facing his enemies, bade them come against him again in their troops, many against one. 'You have offered me your protection,' he said, 'and I would not endure it, but now I swear to you by all my gods that you and I do not part this day till you have accepted my protection, or till I lie without life on this lawn a trophy of your prowess and a monument of the chivalry and hospitality of the Red Branch.' Then a boy stood out from the rest. He was freckled, and with red hair, and his voice was loud and fierce.

'Thou shalt have a comrade in thy battle henceforward,' he said, 'O brave stranger. On the banks of the Nemnich,[28] where it springs beneath my father's dun on the Hill of Gabra, nigh Tara, I met a prophetess; Acaill is her name, the wisest of all women; and I asked her who would be my life-friend. And she answered, "I see him standing against a green wall at Emain Macha, at bay, with the blood and soil of battle upon him, and alone he gives challenge to a multitude. He is thy life-friend, O Laeg," she said, "and no man ever had a friend like him or will till the end of time."'

So saying he ran to Setanta, and kneeling down he took him by his right hand, and said, 'I am thy man from this day forward.' And after that he arose and kissed him, and standing by his side cried, 'O Cumascra Mend Macha, O stammering son of Concobar, if ever I was a shield to thee against thy mockers, come hither; and thou too come O Art Storm-Ear, and thou Art of the Shadow, and thou O Fionn of the Songs, and you O Ide and Sheeling, who were nursed at the same breast and knee with myself.' So he summoned to him his friends, and they came to him, and there came to him, uninvited, the three sons of Fergus and others whose hearts were stirred with shame or ruth. Yet, indeed, they were few compared with the multitude of his enemies. Then for the first time the boy's soul was confused, and he cried aloud, and bowed his head between his hands, and the hot tears gushed forth like rain from his eyes, mingled with blood. Soon, hearing the loud mockery and derisive laughter of his enemies, he hardened his heart and went out against them with these his friends, and drove them over the whole course of the playing-ground, and, hard by the north goal, he brake the battle upon them and they fled. Of the fugitives some ran round the King and the Champion where they sat, but Setanta running straight sprang lightly over the chess table. Then Concobar, reaching forth his left hand, caught him by the wrist and brought him to a stand, panting and with dilated eyes.

'Why art thou so enraged?' said the King, 'and why dost thou so maltreat my boys?'

It was a long time before the boy answered, so furiously burned the battle-fire within him, so that the King repeated his question more than once. At last he made answer –

'Because they have not treated me with the respect due a stranger.'

'Who art thou thyself?' said the King.

'I am Setanta, son of Sualtam and of Dectera thy own sister, and it is not before my uncle's palace that I should be dishonoured.'

Concobar smiled, for he was well pleased with the appearance and behaviour of the boy, but Fergus caught him up in his great arms and kissed him, and he said –

'Dost thou know me, O Setanta?'

'I think thou art Fergus Mac Roy,' he answered.

'Wilt thou have me for thy tutor?' said Fergus.

'Right gladly,' answered Setanta. 'For in that hope too I left Dun Dalgan, coming hither secretly without the knowledge of my parents.'

This was the first martial exploit of Setanta, who is also called Cuculain, and the reward of this his first battle was that the boys at his uncle's school elected him to be for their captain, and one and all they put themselves under his protection. And a gentle captain made he when the war-spirit went out of him, and a good play-fellow and comrade was Setanta amongst his new friends.

That night Setanta and Laeg slept in the same bed of healing after the physicians had dressed their wounds; and they related many things to each other, and oft times they kissed one another with great affection, till sweet sleep made heavy their eyelids.

So, impelled by the unseen, Setanta came to Emain Macha without the knowledge of his parents, but in fulfilment of the law, for at a certain age all the boys of the Ultonians should come thither to associate there with their equals and superiors, and be instructed by appointed tutors in the heroic arts of war and the beautiful arts of peace. Concobar Mac Nessa was not only King of Ulster and captain of the Red Branch, but was also the head and chief of a great school. In this school the boys did not injure their eyesight and impair their health by poring over books; nor were compelled to learn what they could not understand; nor were instructed by persons whom they did not wish to resemble. They were taught to hurl spears at a mark; to train war-horses and guide war-chariots; to lay on with the sword and defend themselves with sword and shield; to cast the hand-stone of the warrior – a great art in those days;

to run, to leap, and to swim; to rear tents of turf and branches swiftly, and to roof them with sedge and rushes; to speak appropriately with equals and superiors and inferiors, and to exhibit the beautiful practices of hospitality according to the rank of guests, whether kings, captains, warriors, bards or professional men, or unknown wayfarers; and to play at chess and draughts, which were the chief social pastimes of the age; and to drink and be merry in hall, but always without intoxication; and to respect their plighted word and be ever loyal to their captains; to reverence women, remembering always those who bore them and suckled when they were themselves helpless and of no account; to be kind to the feeble and unwarlike; and, in short, all that it became brave men to feel and to think and to do in war and in peace. Also there were those who taught them the history of their ancestors, the great names of the Clanna Rury, and to distinguish between those who had done well and those who had not done so well, and the few who had done ill. And these their several instructors appointed by Concobar Mac Nessa and the council of his wise men were famous captains of the Ultonians, and approved bards and historians. And over all the high king of Ulster, Concobar Mac Nessa, was chief and president, not in name only but in fact, being well aware of all the instructors and all the instructed, and who was doing well and exhibiting heroic traits, and who was doing ill, tending downwards to the vast and slavish multitude whose office was to labour and to serve and in no respect to bear rule, which is for ever the office of the multitude in whose souls no god has kindled the divine fire by which the lamp of the sun, and the candles of the stars, and the glory and prosperity of nations are sustained and fed. Such, and so supervised, was the Royal School of Emain Macha in the days when Concobar Mac Nessa was King, and when Fergus Mac Roy Champion, and when the son of Sualtam, not yet known by his rightful name, was a pupil of the same and under tutors and governors like the rest, though his fond mother would have evaded the law, for she loved him dearly, and feared for him the rude companionship and the stern discipline, the early rising and the strong labours of the great school.

VI

THE SMITH'S SUPPER PARTY

'Bearing on shoulders immense
Atlantean the weight,
Well nigh not to be borne,
Of the too vast orb of her fate.'
MATTHEW ARNOLD.

One day, in the forenoon, a man came to Emain Macha. He was grim and swarthy, with great hands and arms. He made no reverence to Concobar or to any of the Ultonians, but standing stark before them, spake thus, not fluently: – 'My master, Culain, high smith of all Ulster, bids thee to supper this night, O Concobar; and he wills thee to know that because he has not wide territories, and flocks, and herds, and tribute-paying peoples, only the implements of his industry, his anvils and hammers and tongs, and the slender profits of his labour, he feareth to feast all the Red Branch, who are by report mighty to eat and to drink; he would not for all Ireland bring famine upon his own industrious youths, his journeymen and his apprentices. Come therefore with a choice selection of thy knights, choosing those who are not great eaters, and drinkers, and you shall all have a fair welcome, a goodly supper, and a proportionate quantity of drink.' That speech was a cause of great mirth to the Ultonians; nevertheless they restrained their laughter, so that the grim ambassador, who seemed withal to be a very angry man, saw nothing but grave countenances. Concobar answered him courteously, saying that he accepted the invitation, and that he would be mindful of the smith's wishes. When the man departed the

Red Branch gave a loose rein to their mirth, each man charging the other with being in especial the person whose presence would be a cause of sorrow to the smith.

Culain was a mighty craftsman in those days. It was he who used to make weapons, armour, and chariots for the Ultonians, and there was never in Ireland a better smith than he. In his huge and smoky dun the ringing of hammers and the husky roar of the bellows seldom ceased; even at night the red glare of his furnaces painted far and wide the barren moor where he dwelt. Herdsmen and shepherds who, in quest of estrays, found themselves unawares in this neighbourhood, fled away praying to their gods, and, as they ran, murmured incantations.

In the afternoon Concobar, having made as good a selection as he could of his chief men, set forth to go. As they passed through the lawn he saw Setanta playing with his comrades. He stopped for a while to look, and then called the lad, who came at once and stood erect and silent before the King. He was now full ten years of age, straight and well-made and with sinews as hard as tempered steel. When he saw the company looking at him, he blushed, and his blushing became him well.

'Culain the smith,' said Concobar, 'hath invited us to a feast. If it is pleasing to thee, come too.'

'It is pleasing indeed,' replied the boy, for he ardently desired to see the famous artificer, his people, his furnaces, and his engines. 'But let me first, I pray thee, see this our game brought to an end, for the boys await my return. After that I will follow quickly, nor can I lose my way upon the moor, for the road hence to the smith's dun is well trodden and scored with wheels, and the sky too at night is red above the city.'

Concobar gave him permission, and Setanta hastened back to his playmates, who hailed him gladly in his returning, for they feared that the King might have taken him away from them.

The King and his great men went away eastward after that and they conversed eagerly by the way, talking sometimes of a certain recent great rebellion of the non-Irian kings of Ulla,[29] and of each other's prowess and the prowess of the insurgents, and sometimes of the smith and his strange and unusual invitation.

'Say no word and do no thing,' said Concobar, 'at which even a

THE SMITH'S SUPPER PARTY

very angry and suspicious man might take offence, for as to our host and his artificers, their ways are not like ours, or their thoughts like our thoughts, and they are a great and formidable people.'

The Red Branch did not relish that speech, for they thought that under the measureless canopy of the sky there were no people great or formidable but themselves.

VII

SETANTA AND THE SMITH'S DOG

> 'How he fell
> From heaven, they fabled, thrown by angry Jove
> Sheer o'er the crystal battlements; from morn
> To noon, from noon to dewy eve,
> A Summer's day, he fell; and with the setting sun
> Dropped from the zenith like a falling star,
> On Lemnos.'
>
> MILTON.

When Culain saw far away the tall figures of the Ultonians against the sunset, and the flashing of their weapons and armour, he cried out with a loud voice to his people to stop working and slack the furnaces and make themselves ready to receive the Red Branch; and he bade the household thralls prepare the supper, roast, boiled and stewed, which he had previously ordered. Then he himself and his journeymen and apprentices stripped themselves, and in huge keeves of water filled by their slaves they washed from them the smoke and sweat of their labour and put on clean clothes. The mirrors at which they dressed themselves were the darkened waters of their enormous tubs.

Culain sent a party of his men and those who were the best dressed and the most comely and who were the boldest and most eloquent in the presence of strangers, to meet the high King of the Ultonians on the moor, but he himself stood huge in the great doorway just beyond the threshold and in front of the bridge over which the Red Branch party was to pass. He had on him over his clothes a clean leathern apron which was not singed or scored. It was fastened at his shoulders and half covered his enormous hairy chest, was girt again at his waist and descended below his knees. He stood with one knee crooked, leaning upon a long ash-handled sledge with a head of glittering bronze. There he gave a friendly and grave welcome to the King and to all the knights one by one. It was dusk when Concobar entered the dun.

'Are all thy people arrived?' said the smith.

'They are,' said Concobar.

Culain bade his people raise the drawbridge which spanned the deep black moat surrounding the city, and after that, with his own hands he unchained his one dog. The dog was of great size and fierceness. It was supposed that there was no man in Ireland whom he could not drag down. He had no other good quality than that he was faithful to his master and guarded his property vigilantly at night. He was quick of sight and hearing and only slept in the daytime. Being let loose he sprang over the moat and three times careered round the city, baying fearfully. Then he stood stiffly on the edge of the moat to watch and listen, and growled at intervals when he heard some noise far away. It was then precisely that Setanta set forth from Emain Macha. Earth quaked to the growling of that ill beast.

In the meantime the smith went into the dun, and when he had commanded his people to light the candles throughout the chamber, he slammed to the vast folding doors with his right hand and his left, and drew forth the massy bar from its place and shot it into the opposing cavity. There was not a knight amongst the Red Branch who could shut one of those doors, using both hands and his whole strength. Of the younger knights, some started to their feet and laid their hands on their sword hilts when they heard the bolt shot.

The smith sat down on his high seat over against Concobar, with his dusky sons and kinsmen around him, and truly they contrasted strangely with the bravery and beauty of the Ultonians. He called for ale, and holding in his hands a huge four-cornered mether of the same, rimmed with silver and furnished with a double silver hand-grip, he

SETANTA AND THE SMITH'S DOG

pledged the King and bade him and his a kindly welcome. He swore, too, that no generation of the children of Rury, and he had wrought for many, had done more credit to his workmanship than themselves, nor had he ever made the appliances of war for any of the Gael with equal pleasure. Concobar, on the other hand, responded discreetly, and praised the smith-work of Culain, praising chiefly the shield called Ocean[30], which was one of the wonders of the north-west of Europe. The smith and all his people were well pleased at that speech, and Culain bade his thralls serve supper, which proved to be a very noble repast. There was enough and to spare for all the Ultonians. When supper was ended, the heroes and the artificers pledged each other many times and drank also to the memory of famous men of yore and their fathers who begat them, as was right and customary; and they became very friendly and merry without intoxication, for intoxication was not known in the age of the heroes.

Then said Concobar: 'We have this night toasted many heroes who are gone, and, as it is not right that we should praise ourselves, I propose that we drink now to the heroes that are coming, both those unborn, and those who, still being boys, are under tutors and instructors; and for this toast I name the name of my nephew Setanta, son of Sualtam, who, if any, will one day, O Culain, if I mistake not, illustrate in an unexampled manner thy skill as an artificer of weapons and armour.'

'Is he then a boy of that promise, O Concobar?' said the smith, 'for if he is I am truly rejoiced to hear it.'

'He is all that I say,' answered the King somewhat hotly, 'and of a beauty corresponding. And of that thou shalt be the judge to-night, for he is coming, and indeed I am momentarily expecting to hear the loud clamour of his brazen hurle upon the doors of the dun, after his having leapt at one bound both thy moat and thy rampart.'

The smith started from his high seat uttering a great oath, such as men used then, and sternly chid Concobar because he had said that all his people had arrived. 'If the boy comes now,' he said, 'ere I can chain the dog, verily he will be torn into small pieces.'

Just then they heard the baying of the dog sounding terribly in the hollow night, and every face was blanched throughout the vast

47

chamber. Then without was heard a noise of trampling feet and short furious yells and sibilant gaspings, as of one who exerts all his strength, after which a dull sound at which the earth seemed to shake, mingled with a noise of breaking bones, and after that silence. Ere the people in the dun could do more than look at each other speechless, they heard a clear but not clamorous knocking at the doors of the dun. Some of the smith's young men back-shot the bolt and opened the doors, and the boy Setanta stepped in out of the night. He was very pale. His scarlet mantle was in rags and trailing, and his linen tunic beneath and his white knees red with blood, which ran down his legs and over his bare feet. He made a reverence, as he had been taught, to the man of the house and to his people, and went backwards to the upper end of the chamber. The Ultonians ran to meet him, but Fergus Mac Roy was the first, and he took Setanta upon his mighty shoulder and bore him along and set him down at the table between himself and the King.

'Did the dog come against thee?' said Culain.

'Truly he came against me,' answered the boy.

'And art thou hurt?' cried the smith.

'No, indeed,' answered Setanta, 'but I think he is.'

At that moment a party of the smith's people entered the dun bearing between them the carcass of the dog from whose mouth and white crooked fangs the blood was gushing in red torrents; and they showed Culain how the skull of the dog and his ribs had been broken in pieces by some mighty blow, and his backbone also in divers places. Also they said: 'One of the great brazen pillars which stand at the bridge head is bent awry, and the clean bronze denied with blood, and it was at the foot of that pillar we found the dog.' So saying, they laid the body upon the heather in front of Culain's high seat, that it might be full in his eye, and when they did so and again sat down, there was a great silence in the chamber.

VIII

SETANTA, THE PEACE-MAKER

'The swine-herd[31] of Bove Derg, son of the Dagda,
The feasts to which he came used to end in blood.'

GAELIC BARD.

Culain sat silent for a long time looking out before him with eyes like iron, and when at last he spoke his voice was charged with wrath and sorrow.

'O Concobar,' he said, 'and you, the rest, nobles of the children of Rury. You are my guests to-night, wherefore it is not lawful that I should take vengeance upon you for the killing of my brave and faithful hound, who was a better keeper of my treasures than a company of hired warriors. Truly he cost me nothing but his daily allowance of meat, and there was not his equal as a watcher and warder in the world. An eric, therefore, I must have. Consult now together concerning its amount and let the eric be great and conspicuous, for, by Orchil[32] and all the gods who rule beneath the earth, a small eric I will not accept.'

Concobar answered straight, 'Thou shalt not get from me or from the Ultonians any eric, small or great. My nephew slew the beast in fair fight, defending his life against an aggressor. But I will say something else, proud smith, and little it recks me whether it is pleasing to thee or not. Had thy wolf slain my nephew not one of you would have left this dun alive, and of your famous city of artificers I would have made a smoking heap.'

The Ultonians fiercely applauded that speech, declaring that the smiths should get no eric, great or small, for the death of their monster.

The smiths thereupon armed themselves with their hammers, and tongs, and fire-poles, and great bars of unwrought brass, and Culain himself seized an anvil withal to lay waste the ranks of the Red Branch. The Ultonians on their side ran to the walls and plucked down their spears from the pegs, and they raised their shields and balanced their long spears, and swords flashed and screeched as they rushed to light out of the scabbards, and the vast chamber glittered with shaking bronze and shone with the eyeballs of angry men, and rang with shouts of defiance and quick fierce words of command. For the Red Branch embattled themselves on one side of the chamber and the smiths upon the other, burning with unquenchable wrath, earth-born. The vast and high dome re-echoing rang with the clear terrible cries of the Ultonians and the roar of the children of the gloomy Orchil, and, far away, the magic shield moaned at Emain Macha, and the waves of the ocean sent forth a cry, for the peril of death and of shortness of life were around Concobar in that hour. And, though the doors of thick oak, brass-bound, were shut and barred, there came a man into the assembly, and he was not seen. He was red all over, both flesh and raiment, as if he had been plunged in a bath of blood. His countenance was distraught and his eyes like those of an insane man, and sparks new from them like sparks from a smith's stithy when he mightily hammers iron plucked white from the furnace. Smoke and fire came from his mouth. He held in his hand a long boar-yard. The likeness of a boar bounded after him. He traversed the vast chamber with the velocity of lightning, and with his boar-yard beat such as were not already drunk with wrath and battle-fury, and shot insane fire into their souls.[33]

Then indeed it wanted little, not the space of time during which a man might count ten, for the beginning of a murder grim and great as any renowned in the world's chronicles, and it is the opinion of the learned that, in spite of all their valour and beautiful weapons, the artificers would then and there have made a bloody end of the Red Branch had the battle gone forward. But at this moment, ere the first missile was hurled on either side, the boy Setanta sprang into the midst, into the middle space which separated the enraged men, and cried aloud, with a clear high voice that rang distinct above the tumult –

SETANTA, THE PEACE-MAKER

'O Culain, forbear to hurl, and restrain thy people, and you the Ultonians, my kinsmen, delay to shoot. To thee, O chief smith, and thy great-hearted artificers I will myself pay no unworthy eric for the death of thy brave and faithful hound. For verily I will myself take thy dog's place, and nightly guard thy property, sleepless as he was, and I will continue to do so till a hound as trusty and valiant as the hound whom I slew is procured for thee to take his place, and to relieve me of that duty. Truly I slew not thy hound in any wantonness of superior strength, but only in the defence of my own life, which is not mine but my King's. Three times he leaped upon me with white fangs bared and eyes red with murder, and three times I cast him off, but when the fourth time he rushed upon me like a storm, and when with great difficulty I had balked him on that occasion also, then I took him by the throat and by his legs and flung him against one of the brazen pillars withal to make him stupid. And truly it was not my intention to kill him and I am sorry that he is dead, seeing that he was so faithful and so brave, and so dear to thee whom I have always honoured, even when I was a child at Dun Dalgan, and whom, with thy marvel-working craftsman, I have for a long time eagerly desired to see. And I thought that our meeting, whensoever it might be, would be other than this and more friendly.'

As he went on speaking the fierce brows of the smith relaxed, and first he regarded the lad with pity, being so young and fair, and then with admiration for his bravery. Also he thought of his own boyish days, and as he did so a torrent of kindly affection and love poured from his breast towards the boy, yea, though he saw him standing before him with the blood of his faithful hound gilding his linen lena and his white limbs. Yet, indeed, it was not the hound's blood which was on the boy, but his own, so cruelly had the beast torn him with his long and strong and sharp claws.

'That proposal is pleasing to me,' he said, 'and I will accept the eric, which is distinguished and conspicuous and worthy of my greatness and of my name and reputation amongst the Gael. Why should a man be angry for ever when he who did the wrong offers due reparation?' Therewith over his left shoulder he flung the mighty anvil into the dark end of the vast chamber among the furnaces, at the sound of whose falling the solid earth shook. On the other hand Concobar rejoiced at this happy termination of the quarrel, for well he knew the might of those huge children of the gloomy Orchil. He perceived, too, that he could with safety entrust the keeping of the lad to those people, for he saw the smith's countenance when it changed, and he knew that among those artificers there was no guile.

'It is pleasing to me, too,' he said, 'and I will be myself the lad's security for the performance of his promise.'

'Nay, I want no security,' answered the smith. 'The word of a scion of the Red Branch is security enough for me.'

Thereafter all laid aside their weapons and their wrath. The smiths with a mighty clattering cast their tools into the dark end of the chamber, and the Ultonians hanged theirs upon the walls, and the feasting and pledging and making of friendly speeches were resumed. There was no more any anger anywhere, but a more unobstructed flow of mutual good-will and regard, for the Ultonians felt no more a secret inclination to laugh at the dusky artificers, and the smiths no longer regarded with disdain the beauty, bravery, and splendour of the Ultonians.

In the meantime Setanta had returned to his place between the King and Fergus Mac Roy. There a faintness came upon him, and a great horror overshadowed him owing to his battle with the dog, for indeed it was no common dog, and when he would have fallen, owing to the faintness, they pushed him behind them so that he lay at full length upon the couch unseen by the smiths. Concobar nodded to his chief Leech, and he came to him with his instruments and salves and washes. There unobserved he washed the cruel gashes cut by the hound's claws, and applied salves and stitched the skin over the wounds, and, as he did so, in a low voice he murmured healing songs of power.

'Where is the boy?' said Culain.

'He is reposing a little,' said Concobar, 'after his battle and his conflict.'

After a space they gave Setanta a draught of mighty ale, and his heart revived in him and the colour returned to his cheeks wherein before was the pallor of death, and he sat up again in his place, slender and fair, between Concobar and Fergus Mac Roy. The smiths cried

SETANTA, THE PEACE-MAKER

out a friendly welcome to him as he sat up, for they held him now to be their foster-son, and Culain himself stood up in his place holding in both hands a great mether[34] of ale, and he drank to all unborn and immature heroes, naming the name of Setanta, son of Sualtam, now his dear foster-son, and magnified his courage, so that the boy blushed vehemently and his eyelids trembled and drooped; and all the artificers stood up too and drank to their foster-son, wishing him victory and success, and they drained their goblets and dashed them, mouth downwards, upon the brazen tables, so that the clang reverberated over Ulla. Setanta thereupon stood up while the smiths roared a welcome to their foster-son, and he said that it was not he who had gained the victory, for that someone invisible had assisted him and had charged him with a strength not his own. Then he faltered in his speech and said again that he would be a faithful hound in the service of the artificers, and sat down. The smiths at that time would not have yielded him for all the hounds in the world.

After that their harpers harped for them and their story tellers related true stories, provoking laughter and weeping. There was no story told that was not true in the age of the heroes. Then the smiths sang one of their songs of labour, though it needed the accompaniment of ringing mettle, a song wild and strange, and the Ultonians clear and high sang all together with open mouths a song of battle and triumph and of the marching home to Emain Macha with victory; and so they spent the night, till Concobar said –

'O Culain, feasting and singing are good, but slumber is good also. Dismiss us now to our rest and our slumber, for we, the Red Branch, must rise betimes in the morning, having our own proper work to perform day by day in Emain Macha, as you yours in your industrious city.'

With difficulty were the smiths persuaded to yield to that request, for right seldom was there a feast in Dun Culain, and the unusual pleasure and joyful sense of comradeship and social exaltation were very pleasing to their hearts.

The Ultonians slept that night in the smiths' hall upon resplendent couches which had been prepared for them, and early in the morning, having taken a friendly leave of the artificers, they departed, leaving the lad behind them asleep. Setanta remained with the smiths a long time after that, and Culain and his people loved him greatly and taught him many things. It was owing to this adventure and what came of it that Setanta got his second name, viz., the Hound of Culain or Cu-Culain. Under that name he wrought all his marvellous deeds.

IX

THE CHAMPION AND THE KING

> 'Sing, O Muse, the destructive wrath of Achilles, son
> of Peleus, which brought countless woes upon the
> Achaeans.'
>
> HOMER.

Concobar Mac Nessa sat one day in his high chair, judging the Ultonians. His great Council sat before him. In the Champion's throne sat Fergus Mac Roy. Before the high King his suitors gave testimony and his brehons pleaded, and Concobar in each case pronounced judgment, clearly and intelligently, briefly and concisely, with learning and with equity.

'Right glad am I, O Concobar,' said Fergus, 'that thou art in the King's throne, and I where I sit. Verily, had I remained in that chair of honour and distress, long since would these historians and poets and subtle-minded lawyers have talked and rhymed me into madness, or into my grave.'

Concobar made answer – 'Dear foster-father, the high gods in their wisdom have fashioned us each man to illustrate some virtue. To thee they have given strength, courage, and magnanimity above all others; and to me, in small measure, the vision of justice, and the perception of her beautiful laws. A man can only excel in what he loves, and verily I love well the known laws of the Ultonians.'

A great man just then entered the hall. His mantle was black. In the breast of it, instead of a brooch, he wore an iron pin. He came swiftly and without making the customary reverences. His face was pale, and his garments torn, his dark-grey tunic stained with blood. He stood in the midst and cried –

'O high King of the Ultonians, and you the wise men and sages of the children of Rury, to all of you there is now need of some prudent resolution. A great deed has been done in Ulla.'

'What is that?' said the King.

'The abduction of the Beautiful Woman by Naysi, son of Usna. Verily, she is taken away and may not be recovered, for the Clan Usna came last night with a great company to the dun and they stormed it in their might and their valour, and their irresistible fury, and they have taken away Deirdré in their swift chariots, and have gone eastwards to the Muirnicht with intent to cross the sea northwards, and abide henceforth with their prize in the land of the Picts and of the Albanah, beyond the stormy currents of the Moyle.'

Fergus Mac Roy, when he heard that word, sat up with eyes bright-blazing in his head. Dearer to him than all the rest were those sons of Usna, namely – Naysi, Anli, and Ardane, and dearest of the three was Naysi, who excelled all the youth of his time in beauty, valour, and accomplishments.

'Bind that man!' cried Concobar. His voice rang terribly through the vast chamber. Truly it sheared through men's souls like a dividing sword.

His guards took the man and bound him. 'Lead him away now,' said Concobar, 'and stone him with stones even to the parting of body with soul.'

The man was one of Deirdré's guard.

A great silence fell upon the assembly after that and no man spoke, only they looked at the King and then again at the Champion, and, as it were, questioned one another silently with their eyes. It was the silence behind which run the Fomorh, brazen-throated and clad with storm. Well knew those wise men that what they long apprehended had come now to pass, namely, the fierce and truceless antagonism of the King and of the ex-King. Well they knew that Concobar would not forgive the Clan Usna, and that Fergus Mac Roy would not permit them to be punished. Therefore, great and mighty as were the men,

THE CHAMPION AND THE KING

yet on this occasion they might be likened only to cattle who stand aside astonished when two fierce bulls, rending the earth as they come, advance against each other for the mastery of the herd. In the high King's face the angry blood showed as two crimson spots one on either cheek, and his eyes, harder than steel, sparkled under brows more rigid than brass. On the other hand, the face of the Champion darkened as the sea darkens when a black squall descends suddenly upon its sunny and glittering tides, wrinkling and convulsing all the face of the deep. His listlessness and amiability alike went out of him, and he sat huge and erect in his throne. His mighty chest expanded and stood out like a shield, and the muscles of his neck, stronger than a bull's, became clear and distinct, and his gathering ire and stern resolution rushed stormfully through his nostrils. The King first spoke.

'To the man who has broken our law and abducted the child of ill omen, I decree death by the sword and burial with the three throws of dishonour, and if taken alive, then death by burning with the same, and if he escapes out of Erin, then sentence of perpetual banishment and expatriation.'

'He shall not be slain, and he shall not be burned, and he shall not be exiled. I say it, even I, Fergus, son of the Red Rossa, Champion of the North. Let the man who will gainsay me show himself now in Emain Macha. Let him bring round the buckle of his belt.'

His eyes, as he spoke, were like flames of fire under a forehead dark crimson, and with his clenched fist he struck the brazen table before his throne, so that the clang and roar of the quivering bronze sounded through all the borders of Ulla.

'I will gainsay thee, O Fergus,' cried the King, 'I am the guardian and the executor of the laws of the Ultonians, and those laws shall prevail over thee and over all men.'

'All laws in restraint of true love and affection are unjust,' said Fergus, 'and the law by which Deirdré was consigned to virginity was the unrighteous enactment of cold-hearted and unrighteous men.'

X

DEIRDRÉ

> 'Beautiful the beginning of love,
> A man and a woman and the birds of Angus above them.'
> GAELIC BARD.

The birth of the child Deirdré, daughter of the chief poet of Ulla, was attended with a great portent, for the child shrieked from the mother's womb. Cathvah and the Druids were consulted concerning that omen. They addressed themselves to their art of divination, and having consulted their oracles and gods and familiar spirits, they gave a clear counsel to the Ultonians

'This child,' they said, 'will become a woman, in beauty surpassing all the women who have ever been born or will be born. Her union with a man will be a cause of great sorrow to the Ultonians. Let her, therefore, be exposed after birth; or, if you would not slay the Arch-Poet's only child, let her be sternly immured; let her be reared to womanhood in utter and complete and inviolable solitude, and live and die in her virginity.'

The Ultonians determined that the child should live and be immured. These things took place in the reign of Factna the Righteous, father of Concobar. When the child was born she was called Deirdré. The Ultonians appointed for her a nurse and tutoress named Levarcam. They built for her and for the nurse a strong dun in a remote forest and set a ward there, and they made a solemn law enjoining perpetual virginity on the child of ill omen, and the Druids shed a zone of terror round the dun.

CELTIC WARRIORS AND GIANTS

Concobar Mac Nessa in the wide circuit of his thoughts consulted always for the inviolability of that law, and the stern maintenance of the watching and warding.

Unseen and unobserved, forgotten by all save the wise elders of the Ultonians and by Concobar their King, whose thoughts ranged on all sides devising good for the Red Branch, the child Deirdré grew to be a maiden. Though her beauty was extraordinary, yet her mind was as beautiful as her form, so that the Lady Levarcam loved her exceedingly.

One day when the first flush of early womanhood came upon the maiden, she said to her tutoress as they sat together and conversed –

'Are all men like those our guards who defend us against savage beasts and the merciless Fomorians, dear Levarcam?'

'Those our guards are true and brave men,' said Levarcam.

'Surely they are,' said the girl, 'and we lack no courtesy and due attention at their hands, but dear foster-mother, my question is not answered. Maybe it is not to be answered and that I am curious overmuch. Are all men grim, grave, and austere, wearing rugged countenances scored with ancient wounds, and bearing each man upon his shoulders the weight of some fearful responsibility? Are all men like that, dear Levarcam?'

'Nay, indeed,' said the other, 'there are youths too, gracious, and gay, and beautiful, as well as grave men such as these.'

They sat together in their sunny grianan,[35] embroidering while they conversed. It was early morning and the air was full of the noises and odours of sweet spring-time.

'I know that now,' said the maiden, 'which I only guessed before, for waking or sleeping I have dreamed of a youth who was as unlike these men as the rose-tree with its roses is unlike the rugged oak-tree or the wrinkled pine that has wrestled with a thousand storms. I would wish to have him for a playfellow and pleasant acquaintance. Of maidens, too, such as myself I have dreamed, yet they do not appear to me to be so alluring or so amiable as that youth.'

'Describe him more particularly,' said Levarcam. 'Tell me his tokens one by one that I may know.'

DEIRDRÉ

'He is tall and strong but very graceful in all his motions; and of speech and behaviour both gay and gracious. He is white and ruddy, whiter than snow and ruddier than the rose or the fox-glove, where the heroic blood burns bright in his comely cheeks. His eyes are blue-black under fine and even brows and his hair is a wonder, so dense is it, so lustrous and so curling, blacker than the crow's wing, more shining than the bright armour of the chaffer. His body is broad above and narrow below, strong to withstand and agile to pursue. His limbs long and beautifully proportioned; his hands and feet likewise, and his step elastic Smiles seldom leave his eyes and lips, and his mouth is a fountain of sweet speech. O that I were acquainted with him and he with me? I think we should be happy in each other's company. I think I could love him as well as I do thee, dear foster-mother.'

As she spoke, Deirdré blushed, and first she stooped down over her work and then put before her face and eyes her two beautiful hands, rose-white, with long delicate nails pink-flushed and transparent; and tears, clearer than dewdrops, gushed between her ringers and fell in bright showers upon the embroidery. Then she arose and flung her soft white arms around Levarcam and wept on her bosom.

'There is one youth only amongst the Red Branch,' said Levarcam, 'who answers to that description, namely Naysi, the son of Usna, who is the battle-prop of the Ultonians and the clear-shining torch of their valour, and what god or druid or power hath set that vision before thy mind, I cannot tell.'

'Would that I could see him with eyes and have speech with him,' answered the girl. 'If but once he smiled upon me and I heard the sweet words flow from his mouth which is beyond price, then gladly would I die!'

'Thou shall both see him and have speech with him, O best, sweetest, dearest, and loveliest of all maidens. Truly I will bring him to thee and thee to him, for there is with me power beyond the wont of women.'

Now Levarcam was a mighty Druidess amongst the Ultonians. So the lady in whom they trusted forgot the ancient prophecies and the stern commands of the Red Branch and of their King, owing to the great love which she bore to the maiden and the great compassion which grew upon her day by day, as she observed the life of the solitary girl and thought of the cruel law to which all her youth and beauty and wealth of sweet love beyond all the jewels of the world were thus barbarously sacrificed by the Ultonians in obedience to soothsayers and Druids.

Naysi, son of Usna, once in a hunting became separated from his companions. He wandered far in that forest, seeking some one who should direct him upon his way. Oftentimes he raised his voice, but there was no answer. Such were his beauty, his grace, and his stature, that he seemed more like a god than a man, and such another as Angus Ogue, son of Dagda,[36] whose fairy palace is on the margin of the Boyne. His head and his feet were bare. His short hunting-cloak was dark-red with flowery devices along the edge. On his breast he wore a brooch of gold bronze; carbuncles and precious stones were set in the bronze, and it was carved all over with many spiral devices. His shirt below the mantle was coloured like the tassels of the willow trees. His hair was fastened behind with a clasp and an apple of red gold, and that apple lay below the blades of his ample shoulders. In one hand he bore a broken leash of red bronze, and in the other two hunting spears with blades of flashing findruiney and the hafts were long, slender, and shining. By his thigh hung a short sword in a sheath of red yew and beside it the polished and nigh transparent horn of the Urus, suspended in a baldrick of knitted thread of bronze. The grass stood erect from the pressure of his light feet. His manly face had not yet known the razor; only the first soft down of budding manhood was seen there. His countenance was pure and joyous with bright beaming eyes, and his complexion red and white and of a brilliancy beyond words. In his heart was no guile, only indomitable valour and truth and loyalty and sweet affection. He had never known woman save in the way of courtesy. The very trees and rocks and stones seemed to watch him as he passed.

Then suddenly and unawares an ice-cold air struck chill into his inmost being, the bright earth was obscured and the sun grew dark in the heavens and menacing voices were heard and horrid forms of evil, monstrous, not to be described, came against him, and they bade him return as he had come or they would tear him limb from limb in that forest. Yet the son of Usna was by no means dismayed, only he flushed with wrath and scorn and he drew his sword and went on against the phantoms. In truth Naysi was at that moment passing through the zone of terror which the Ultonian Druids had shed around the dun where Deirdré was immured. The phantoms gave way before him and Naysi passed beyond the zone. 'Surely,' he said, 'there is some chief jewel of the jewels of the world preserved in this place.'

He came to an opening in the forest. Beyond it there was a great space which was cleared and girt all round by trees. There was a dun in its midst. Scarlet and white were the walls of that dun. There was a watch-tower on one side of the dun and a man there sitting in the watchman's seat; a grianan on the other with windows of glass. The roof of the dun was covered all over with feathers of birds of various hues, and shone with a hundred colours. The doorway was the narrowest which Naysi had ever seen. The door pillars were of red yew curiously carved, having feet of bronze and capitals of carved silver, and the lintel above was a straight bar of pure silver. A knotted band or thickening ran round the walls of the dun like a variegated zone, for the colours of it were many and each different from the colours on the walls. In the world there was no such prison as there was no such captive as that prison held. Armed men of huge stature and terrible aspect went round the dun. Their habiliments were black, their weapons without ornament, the pins of their mantles were of iron. With each company went a slinger having his sling bent, an iron bolt in the sling, and his thumb in the string-loop, men who never missed their mark and never struck aught, whether man or beast, that they did not slay. Great hounds such as were not known amongst the Ultonians went with those men. They were grey above and tawny beneath, as large as wild oxen after the growth of one year. They were quick of sight and scent, fiercer than dragons and swifter than eagles; they were not quick of sight and scent to-day. The Lady Levarcam had great power. In and around that dun were three hundred men of war, foreigners, picked men of the great fighting tribes of Banba. Such was the decree of the Ultonians and their wise King, so greatly did they fear concerning those prophecies and omens and concerning the child who in Emain Macha shrieked out of her mother's womb. Naysi regarded the dun with wonder and amazement, and with amazement the astonishing rigour of the watch and ward which were kept there, and the more he looked the more he wondered. It seemed to the hunter that he had chanced upon one of the abodes of the enchanted races of Erin, namely the Tuatha De Dana or the Fomorians, whom the sons of Milesius by their might had driven into the mountains and unfrequented places and who, now immortal and invisible, and possessing great druidic power, were worshipped as gods by the Gael. He knew he was in great peril, but his stout heart did not fail; he was resolved to see this adventure to an end.

As he was about to step out into the open two women came from the door of the grianan. One of them was old; she leaned upon her companion and in her right hand held a long white wand squared save in the middle where it was rounded for the hand grip, very long, unornamented, and unshod at either extremity. Naysi paid slight attention to her, though, as she was the first to come forth, he observed these things. The other was young, tall, slender, and lissom, her raiment costly and splendid like a high queen's on some solemn day, and like a queen's her behaviour and her pacing over the flowery lawn. Never had that hunter seen such a form, so proudly modest and virginal, such sweetness, grace, and majesty of bearing. Presently, having passed a company of the guards, she flung back the white, half-transparent veil that concealed her face. Then the sudden radiance was like the coming unlocked for out of a white cloud of that very bright star which shines on the edge of night and morning. All things were transfigured in her light. Before her the grass grew greener and more glittering and rare flowers started in her way. A silver basket of most delicate craftsmanship, the work of some cunning cerd, was on her right arm. It shone clear and sparkling against her mantle which was exceedingly lustrous, many times folded, darkly crimson, and of substance unknown. She towered above her aged companion, straight as a pillar of red yew in a king's house. So, unwitting, jocund, and innocent, fresh and pure as the morning, she paced over the green lawn, going in the direction of that youth, even Naysi, son of Usna the Ultonian. Naysi's loudly beating heart fell silent when he saw how she came straight towards him; he retreated into the forest, so amazing and so confounding was the radiance of that beauty.

DEIRDRÉ

A company of those grim warders, silent and watchful, followed close upon the women. As they went they slipped the muzzles from the mouths of their dogs and lead them forward leashed. The countenances of the men shewed displeasure. From the tower the watchman cried aloud words in an unknown tongue, hoarse, barbaric accents charged with energy and strong meaning. His voice rang terribly in the hollows of the forest. There was a counter challenge in the forest repeated many times, the voices of men mingled with the baying of hounds. There was a ring of sentinels and dogs far out in the forest. The son of Usna had gone through the ring. For twice seven years and one that astonishing watch and ward had been maintained day and night without relaxation or abatement. When they came to the edge of the forest Levarcam addressed the commander of that company. She said, 'The Lady Deirdré would be alone with me in the forest for a little space to gather flowers and listen to the music of the birds and the stream, relieved, if but for one moment, of this watching and warding.'

The man answered not a word. He was of the Gamanrdians, dwellers by the Sue, which feeds the great Western River;[37] his people were of the Clan Dega in the south, and of the children of Orc[38] from the Isles of Ore in the frozen seas.[39] The blood of the Fomoroh was in those men. The women went on, and that grim company followed, keeping close behind. When they gained the first cover of the trees Levarcam turned round and stretched over them her wand. They stood motionless, both men and dogs. Then the women went forward, and alone.

'Fill thy basket now with forest flowers, O sweetest, and dearest, and fairest of all foster-children, and listen to the songs of the birds and the music of the rill. Cull thy flowers, darling girl, and cull the flower of thy youth, the flower that grows but once for all like thee, the flower whose glory puts high heaven to shame, and whose odour makes mad the most wise.'

'Where shall I gather that flower, O gentlest and most amiable of foster-mothers? Is it in the glade or the thicket, or on the margent of the rill?

'It is not to be found by seeking, O fairest of all maidens. Gather it when thou meetest with it in the way. Wear it in thy heart, be the end what it may. Verily thou wilt not mistake any other flower for that flower.'

'I know not thy meaning, O wise and many-counselled woman, but there is fear upon me, and trembling, and my knees quake at thy strange words. Now, if the whole world were swallowed up I should not be surprised. Surely the end of the world is very nigh.'

'It is the end of the world and the beginning of the world; and the end of life and the beginning of life; and death and life in one, and death and life will soon be the same to thee, O Deirdré!'

'There is amazement upon me, and terror, O my foster-mother, on account of thy words, and on account of the gathering of this flower. Let us return to the dun. Terrible to me are the hollow-sounding ways of the unknown forest.'

'Fear not the unknown forest, O Deirdré. Leave the known and the familiar now that thy time has come. Go on. Accomplish thy destiny. It is vain to strive against fate and the pre-ordained designs of the high gods of Erin. Truly I have failed in my trust. I see great wrath in Emain Macha. I see the Red Branch tossed in storms, and a mighty riving and rending and scattering abroad, and dismal conflagrations, and the blood of heroes falling like rain, and I hear the croaking of Byves.[40] Truly I have proved a brittle prop to the Ultonians, but some power beyond my own drives me on.'

'What wild words are these, O wisest of women, and what this rending and scattering abroad, and showers of blood and croaking of Byves because I cull a flower in the forest?'

'Nay, it is nothing. Have peace and joy while thou canst, sweet Deirdré. Thus I lay my wand upon thy bosom and enjoin peace!'

'Thou art weary, dear foster-mother. Rest thee here now a little space, while I go and gather forest flowers. They are sweeter than those that grow in my garden. O, right glad am I to be alone in the forest, relieved from the observation of those grim-visaged sentinels, to stray solitary in the dim mysterious forest, and to think my own thoughts there, and dream my dreams, and recall that vision which I have seen. O Naysi, son of Usna, sweeter than harps is the mere sound of thy name, O Ultonian!'

Deirdré after that went forward alone into the forest.

DEIRDRÉ

Naysi, when he had started back into the forest stood still for a long time in his retreat. It was the hollow of a tall rock beside a falling stream of water, all flowing snow or transparent crystal. Holly trees and quicken trees grew from its crest, and long twines of ivy fell down before like green torrents. Behind them he concealed himself, when he heard the cries and the challengings and the baying of the hounds. Then he saw the maiden come along the forest glade by the margent of the stream, her basket filled and over-flowing with flowers. The sentient stream sang loud and gay to greet her approaching, with fluent liquid fingers striking more joyously the chords of his stony lyre. Light beyond the sun was shed through the glen before her. Birds, the brightest of plumage and sweetest of note of all the birds of Banba,[41] filled the air with their songs, flying behind her and before her, and on her right hand and on her left. Through his lattice of trailing ivy the son of Usna saw her. Her countenance was purer and clearer than morning-dew upon the rose or the lily, and the rose and lily, nay, the whiteness of the snow of one night and the redness of the reddest rose, were there. Her eyes were blue-black under eyebrows black and fine, but her clustering hair was bright gold, more shining than the gold which boils over the edge of the refiner's crucible. Her forehead was free from all harshness, broad and intelligent, her beautiful smiling lips of the colour of the berries of the mountain ash, her teeth a shower of lustrous pearls. Her face and form, her limbs, hands and feet, were such that no defect, blemish or disproportion could be observed, though one might watch and observe long, seeking to discover them. In that daughter of the High Poet and Historian of the Hound-race of the North,[42] child of valour and true wisdom, the body did not predominate over the spirit, or the spirit over the body, for as her form was of matchless, incomparable, and inexpressible beauty, so her mind was not a whit less well proportioned and refined. Jocund and happy, breathing innocence and love, she came up the dell. The birds of Angus[43] unseen flew above her and shed upon her unearthly graces and charms from the waving of their immortal wings. A silver brooch lay on her breast, the pin of fine bronze ran straight from one shoulder to the other. On her head was a lustrous tyre or leafy diadem shading her countenance, gold above and silver below. Her short kirtle was white below the rose-red mantle, and fringed with gold thread above her perfect and lightly stepping feet. Shoes she wore shining with brightest wire of findruiney. As she came up the dell, rejoicing in her freedom and the sweetness of that sylvan place and the solitude, she contemplated the bright stream, and sang clear and sweet an unpremeditated song.

Naysi stepped forth from his place, putting aside the ivy with his hands, and came down the dell to meet her in her coming. She did not scream or tremble or show any signs of confusion, though she had never before seen any of the youths of the Gael. She only stood still and straight, and with wide eyes of wonder watched him as he drew nigh, for she thought at first that it was the genius of that glen and torrent taking form in reply to her druidic lay. Then when she recognised the comrade and playfellow of her vision, she smiled a friendly and affectionate greeting. On the other hand, Naysi came trembling and blushing. He bowed himself to the earth before her, and kissed the grass before her feet.

They remained together a long time in the glen and told each other all they knew and thought and felt, save one feeling untellable, happy beyond all power of language to express. When Deirdré rose to go, Naysi asked for some token and symbol of remembrance.

As they went she gathered a rose and gave it to Naysi.

'There is a great meaning in this token amongst the youths and maidens of the Gael,' said he.

'I know that,' answered Deirdré. Deirdré returned to Levarcam.

'Thou hast gathered the flower,' said Levarcam.

'I have,' she replied, 'and death and life are one to me now, dear foster-mother.'

Naysi went away through the forest and there is nothing related concerning him till he reached Dun Usna. It was night when he entered the hall. His brothers were sitting at the central fire. Anli was scouring a shield; Ardane was singing the while he polished a spear and held it out against the light to see its straightness and its lustre. They were in no way alarmed about their brother.

'I have seen Deirdré, the daughter of Felim,' he said.

'Then thou art lost!' they answered; the weapons fell from their hands upon the floor.

'I am,' he replied.

'What is thy purpose?' they said.

'To storm the guarded dun, even if I go against it alone, To bear away Deirdré and pass into the land of the Albanagh.'[44]

'Thou shalt not go alone,' they said. 'We have shared in thy glory and thy power, we will share all things with thee.'

They put their right hand into his on that promise. One hundred and fifty nobles of the nobles of that territory did the same, for with Naysi as their captain they did not fear to go upon any enterprise. They knew that expatriation awaited them, but they had rather be with Naysi and his brothers in a strange land than to live without them in Ireland. So the Clan Usna with their mighty men stormed the dun and bore off Deirdré and went away eastward to the Muirnicht. And they crossed the Moyle[45] in ships into the country of the Albanagh, and settled on the delightful shores of Loch Etive and made swordland of the surrounding territory. Great, famous, and long remembered were the deeds of the children of Usna in that land.

XI

THERE WAS WAR IN ULSTER

'Each spake words of high disdain
And insult to his heart's best brother,
They parted ne'er to meet again.'
                              COLERIDGE.

It was on account of this that there arose at first that dissidence and divergence of opinion in the great Council at Emain Macha between Concobar Mac Nessa and Fergus Mac Roy, Concobar standing for the law which he had been sworn to safeguard and to execute, and Fergus casting over the lovers the shield of his name and fame, his authority and his strength, and the singular affection with which he was regarded by all the Ultonians.

After Fergus had made that speech in disparagement and contempt of the solemn enactment and decree in accordance with which Deirdré had been immured, Concobar did not immediately answer, for he knew that he was heated both on account of the abduction and on account of the words of Fergus. Then he said –

'The valour of the Red Branch, whereby we flourish so conspicuously here in the North, doth not spring out of itself, and doth not come by discipline, teaching, and example. It has its root in a virtue of which the bards indeed, for bardic reasons, make little mention though it hold a firm place in the laws of the Ultonians both ancient and recent. This, our valour, and the famous kindred virtues through which we are strong and irresistible, so that the world has today nothing anywhere of equal glory and power, spring from the chastity of our women, which is conspicuous and clear-shining, and in the modesty and shamefastness of our young heroes, and the extreme rarity of lawless relations between men and women in Ulla, the servile tribes excepted, of whom no man maketh any account. Against such lawlessness our wise ancestors have decreed terrible punishments. According to the laws of the Ultonians, those who offend in this respect are burned alive in the place of the burnings, and over their ashes are thrown the three throws of dishonour. And well I know that these laws ofttimes to the unthinking and to those who judge by their affections merely, seem harsh and unnatural. Yea truly, were I not high King, I could weep, seeing gentle youths and maidens, and men and women, whom the singing of Angus Ogue's birds have made mad, led away by my orders to be devoured by flame. But so it is best, for without chastity valour faileth in a nation, and lawlessness in this respect begetteth sure and rapid decay, and I give not this forth as an opinion but as a thing that I know, seeing it as clearly with my mind, O Fergus, as I see with my eyes thy countenance and form and the foldings of thy fuan[46] and the shape and ornamentation of the wheel-brooch upon thy breast. Without chastity there is no enduring valour in a nation. And thou, too, O Fergus, sitting there in the champion's throne, hast more than once or twice heard me pronounce the dread sentence without word of protest or dissent. But now, because it toucheth thee thyself, strongly and fiercely thy voice of protest is lifted up, and unless I and this Council can over-persuade thee, this thy rebellious purpose will be thy own undoing or that of the Red Branch. Are the sons of Usna dear only to thee? I say they are dearer to me, but the Red Branch is still dearer, and it is the destruction of the Red Branch which unwittingly thou wouldst Compass. Nor was that law concerning the inviolable virginity of the child of Felim foolish or unwise, for it was made solemnly by the Ultonians in obedience to the united voice of the Druids of Ulla, men who see deeply into the hidden causes of things and the obscure relations of events, of which we men of war have no perception.'

So spoke Concobar, not threateningly like a sovereign king, but pleadingly. On the other hand Fergus Mac Roy, rearing his huge form, stood upon his feet, and said –

THERE WAS WAR IN ULSTER

'To answer fine reasonings I have no skill, but I swear by the sun and the wind and the earth and by my own right hand, which is a stronger oath than any, that I will bring back the sons of Usna into Ireland, and that they shall live and flourish in their place and sit honourably in this great hall of the Clanna Rury, whether it be pleasing to thee or displeasing. For I take the Clan Usna under my protection from this day forth, and well I know that there is not in Erin or in Alba a man born of a woman, no nor the Tuatha De Danan themselves, who will break through that protection!'

'I will break through it,' said the King.

After that Fergus departed from Emain Macha and went away with his people into the east to his own country. There he debated and considered for a long time, but at last, so great was his affection for the Clan Usna, that he went over the Moyle in ships to the country of the Albanagh and brought home the sons of Usna, and they were slain by Concobar Mac Nessa, according as he had promised by the word of his mouth. Then Fergus rebelled against Concobar, drawing after him two-thirds of the Red Branch, and amongst them Duvac Dael Ulla and Cormac Conlingas, Concobar's own son, and many other great men, but the chiefest and best and most renowned of the Ultonians adhered to the King. The whole province was shaken with war and there was great shedding of blood, but in the end Concobar prevailed and drove out Fergus Mac Roy. After that expulsion Fergus and three thousand of the Red Branch fled across the Shannon and came to Rath Cruhane, and entered into military service with Meave who was the queen of all the country west of the Shannon.

There is nothing told about Cuculain in connection with this war. It is hard to imagine him taking any side in such a war. But, in fact, he was still a schoolboy under tutors and governors and could not lawfully appear in arms, seeing that he was not yet knighted. He was either with the smiths or, having procured a worthy hound to take his place, he had gone back to the royal school at Emain Macha. But the time when Cuculain should be knighted, that is to say, invested with arms, and solemnly received into the Red Branch as man to the high King of all Ulla, now drew on, and such a knighting as that, and under such signs, omens, and portents, has never been recorded anywhere in the history of the nations.

In the meantime, Fergus and his exiles served Queen Meave and were subduing all the rest of Ireland under her authority, so that Meave, Queen of Connaught, became very great and proud, and in the end meditated the overthrow of Ulster and the conquest of the Red Branch. Queen Meave and Fergus leading the joined host of the four remaining provinces, Meath, Connaught, Munster, and Leinster, certain of success owing to a strange lethargy which then fell on the Ultonians, did invade Ulster. But as they drew nigh to the mearings they found the in-gate of the province barred by one man. It is needless to mention that man's name. It was Dethcaen's nursling, the ex-pupil of Fergus Mac Roy, the little boy Setanta grown into a terrible and irresistible hero. It was by his defence of Ulster on that occasion against Fergus and Meave and the four provinces, that Cuculain acquired his deathless glory and became the chief hero of the north-west of the world. So these chapters which relate to the abduction of Deirdré and the rebellion and expulsion of Fergus, are a vital portion of the whole story of Cuculain. We must now return to the hero's schoolboy days which, however, are drawing to a memorable conclusion.

XII

THE SACRED CHARIOT

'He dwelt a while among the neat-herds
Of King Admetus, veiling his godhood.'
GREEK MYTHOLOGY.

'At Tailteen I raced my steeds against a woman,
Though great with child she came first to the goal,
Alas, I knew not the auburn-haired Macha,
Thence came affliction upon the Ultonians.'
CONCOBAR MAC NESSA.

Concobar Mac Nessa on a solemn day called Cuculain forth from the ranks of the boys where they stood in the rear of the assembly and said –

'O Setanta, there is a duty which falls to me by virtue of my kingly office, and therein I need an assistant. For it is my province to keep bright and in good running order the chariot of Macha wherein she used to go forth to war from Emain, and to clean out the corn-troughs of her two steeds and put there fresh barley perpetually, and fresh hay in their mangers. Illan the Fair[47] was my last helper in this office, till the recent great rebellion. That ministry is thine now, if it is pleasing to thee to accept it.'

The boy said that it was pleasing, and the King gave him the key of the chamber in which were the vessels and implements used in discharging that sacred function.

Afterwards, on the same day, the King said to him, 'Wash thyself now in pure water and put on new clean raiment and come again to me.'

The boy washed himself and put on new clean raiment. The King himself did the same.

Concobar said: 'Go now to the chamber of which I have given thee the key and fill with oil the silver oil-can and take a towel of the towels of fawn-skin which are there and return.' He did so; and Concobar and his nephew, armed youths following, went to the house of the chariot.

Ere Concobar turned the wards of the lock he heard voices within in the chariot-house. There, one said to another, 'This is he. Our long watch and ward are near the end.' And the other said, 'It is well. Too long have we been here waiting.'

'Hast thou heard anything, my nephew?' said Concobar.

'I have heard nothing,' said the lad.

Concobar opened the great folding-doors. There was a sound there like glad voices mingled with a roar of revolving wheels, and then silence. Setanta drew back in dismay, and even Concobar stood still. 'I have not observed such portents before in the chariot-house,' he said. The King and his nephew entered the hollow chamber. The chariot was motionless but very bright. One would have said that the bronze burned. It was of great size and beauty. By its side were two horse-stalls with racks and mangers, the bars of the rack were of gold bronze which was called findruiney, and the mangers of yellow brass. The floor was paved with cut marble, the walls lined with smooth boards of ash. There were no windows, but there were nine lamps in the room. 'It will be thy duty to feed those lamps,' said Concobar.

Concobar took the fawn-skin towel from the boy and polished the chariot, and the wheels, tyres, and boxes, and the wheel-spokes. He oiled the wheels too, and mightily lifting the great chariot seized the spokes with his right hand and made the wheels spin.

'Go now to the chamber of which I have given thee the keys,' he said, 'and bring the buckets, and clear out the mangers to the last grain, and empty the stale barley into the place of the burning, and afterwards take fresh barley from the bin which is in the chamber and fill the mangers. Empty the racks also and bring fresh hay. Thou wilt

THE SACRED CHARIOT

find it stored there too; clean straw also and litter the horse-stalls.'

The boy did that. In the meantime Concobar polished the pole, and the yoke, and the chains. From the wall he took the head-gear of the horses and the long shining reins of interwoven brass and did the same very carefully till there was not a speck of rust or discolouration to be seen.

'Where are the horses, my Uncle Concobar?' said the boy.

'That I cannot rightly tell,' said Concobar, 'but verily they are somewhere.'

'What are those horses?' said the boy. 'How are they called? What their attributes, and why do I fill their racks and mangers?'

'They are the Liath Macha and Black Shanglan,' said Concobar. 'They have not been seen in Erin for three hundred years, not since Macha dwelt visibly in Emain as the bride of Kimbaoth, son of Fiontann. In this chariot she went forth to war, charioteering her warlike groom. But they are to come again for the promised one and bear him to battle and to conflict in this chariot, and the time is not known but the King of Emain is under gesa[48] to keep the chariot bright and the racks and mangers furnished with fresh hay, and barley two years old. He is to wait, and watch, and stand prepared under gesa most terrible.'

'Maybe Kimbaoth will return to us again,' said the boy.

'Nay, it hath not been so prophesied,' answered the King. 'He was great, and stern, and formidable. But our promised one is gentle exceedingly. He will not know his own greatness, and his nearest comrades will not know it, and there will be more of love in his heart than war.' So saying Concobar looked steadfastly upon the boy.

'Conall Carnach is as famous for love as for war,' said Setanta. 'He is peerless in beauty, and his strength and courage are equal to his comeliness, and his chivalry and battle-splendour to his strength.'

'Nay, lad, it is not Conall Carnach, though the women of Ulla sicken and droop for the love of him. Verily, it is not Conall Carnach.'

Setanta examined curiously the great war-car.

'Was Kimbaoth assisting his wife,' he asked, 'when she took captive the sons of Dithorba?'

'Nay,' said the King, 'she went forth alone and crossed the Shannon with one step into the land of the Fir-bolgs, and there, one by one, she bound those builder-giants the sons of Dithorba, and bore them hither in her might, and truly those five brethren were no small load for the back of one woman.'

'Has anyone seen her in our time?' asked the lad.

'I have,' said Concobar. 'I saw her at the great fair of Tailteen. There she pronounced a curse upon me and upon the Red Branch.[49] The curse hath not yet fallen, but it will fall in my time, and the promised one will come in my time and he will redeem us from its power. Great tribulation will be his. Question me no more, dear Setanta, I have said more than enough.'

They went forth from the sacred chamber and Concobar locked the doors.

As they crossed the vacant space going to the palace, Concobar said –

'Why art thou sad, dear Setanta?'

'I am not sad,' answered the boy.

'Truly there is no sadness in thy face, or thy lips, in thy voice or thy behaviour, but it is deep down in thine eyes,' said the King. 'I see it there always.'

Setanta laughed lightly. 'I know it not,' he said.

Concobar went his way after that, musing, and Setanta, having replaced the sacred vessels in their chamber and having locked the door, strode away into the boys' hall. There was a great fire in the midst, and the boys sat round it, for it was cold. Cuculain broke their circle, pushing the boys asunder, and sat down. They tried to drag him away, but he laughed and kept his place like a rock. Then they called him 'a Fomorian, and no man', and perforce made their circle wider.

XIII

THE WEIRD HORSES

> 'On the brink of the night and the morning
> My coursers are wont to respire,
> But the earth has just whispered a warning,
> That their flight must be swifter than fire,
> They shall breathe the hot air of desire.'
>
> SHELLEY.

One night when the stars shone brightly, Setanta, as he passed by Cathvah's astrological tower, heard him declare to his students that whoever should be knighted by Concobar on a certain day would be famous to the world's end. He was in his coming out of the forest then with a bundle of young ash trees under his arm. He thought to put them to season and therewith make slings, for truly he surpassed all others in the use of the sling. Setanta went his way after that and came into the speckled house. It was the armoury of the Red Branch and shone with all manner of war-furniture. A fire burned here always, absorbing the damp of the air lest the metal should take rust. Setanta flung his trees into the rafters over the fire very deftly, so that they caught and remained there. He said they would season best in that place.

As he turned to go a man stood before him in the vast and hollow chamber.

'I know thee,' said the boy. 'What wouldst thou now?'

'Thou shalt go forth to-night,' said the man,[50] 'and take captive the Liath Macha and Black Shanghlan. Power will be given to thee. Go out boldly.'

'I am not wont to go out fearfully,' answered the lad. 'Great labours are thrust upon me.'

He went into the supper hall as at other times and took his customary place there, and ate and drank.

'Thy eyes are very bright,' said Laeg.

'They will be brighter ere the day,' he replied.

'That is an expert juggler,' said Laeg. 'How he tosseth the bright balls!'

'Can he toss the stars so?' said Setanta.

'Thou art strange and wild to-night,' said Laeg.

'I will be stranger and wilder ere the morrow,' cried Setanta.

He stood up to go. Laeg caught him by the skirt of his mantle. The piece came away in his hand.

'Whither art thou going, Setanta?' cried the King from the other end of the vast hall.

'To seek my horses,' cried the lad. His voice rang round the hollow dome and down the resounding galleries and long corridors, so that men started in their seats and looked towards him.

'They are stabled since the setting of the sun,' said the chief groom.

'Thou liest,' answered the boy. 'They are in the hills and valleys of Erin.' His eyes burned like fire and his stature was exalted before their eyes.

'Great deeds will be done in Erin this night,' said Concobar.

He went forth into the night. There was great power upon him. He crossed the Plain of the Hurlings and the Plain of the Assemblies and the open country and the great waste moor, going on to Dun-Culain. Culain's new hound cowered low when he saw him. The boy sprang over moat and rampart at one bound and burst open the doors of the smith's house, breaking the bar. The noise of the riven beam was like the brattling of thunder.

'That is an unusual way to enter a man's house,' said Culain. He and his people were at supper.

'It is,' said Setanta. 'Things more unusual will happen this night. Give me bridles that will hold the strongest horses.' Culain gave him two bridles.

THE WEIRD HORSES

'Will they hold the strongest horses?' said the boy.

'Anything less than the Liath Macha they will hold,' said the smith.

The boy snapped the bridles and flung them aside. 'I want bridles that will hold the Liath Macha and Black Shanglan,' said he.

'Fire all the furnaces,' cried Culain. 'Handle your tools; show your might. Work now, men, for your lives. Verily, if he get not the bridles, soon your dead will be more numerous than your living.'

Culain and his people made the bridles. He gave them to Cuculain. The smiths stood around in pallid groups. Cuculain took the bridles and went forth. He went south-westwards to Slieve Fuad, and came to the Grey Lake. The moon shone and the lake glowed like silver. There was a great horse feeding by the lake. He raised his head and neighed when he heard footsteps on the hill. He came on against Cuculain and Cuculain went on against him. The boy had one bridle knotted round his waist and the other in his teeth. He leaped upon the steed and caught him by the forelock and his mouth. The horse reared mightily, but Setanta held him and dragged his head down to the ground. The grey steed grew greater and more terrible. So did Cuculain.

'Thou hast met thy master, O Liath Macha, this night,' he cried. 'Surely I will not lose thee. Ascend into the heavens, or, breaking the earth's roof, descend to Orchil,[51] yet even so thou wilt not shake me away.'

Ireland quaked from the centre to the sea. They reeled together, steed and hero, through the plains of Murthemney. 'Make the circuit of Ireland Liath Macha and I shall be on the neck of thee,' cried Cuculain. The horse went in reeling circles round Ireland. Cuculain mightily thust the bit into his mouth and made fast the headstall. The Liath Macha went a second time round Ireland. The sea retreated from the shore and stood in heaps. Cuculain sprang upon his back. A third time the horse went round Ireland, bounding from peak to peak. They seemed a resplendent Fomorian phantom against the stars. The horse came to a stand. 'I think thou art tamed, O Liath Macha,' said Cuculain. 'Go on now to the Dark Valley.' They came to the Dark Valley. There was night there always. Shapes of Death and Horror, Fomorian apparitions, guarded the entrance. They came against Cuculain, and he went against them. A voice from within cried, 'Forbear, this is the promised one. Your watching and warding are at end.' He rode into the Dark Valley. There was a roaring of unseen rivers in the darkness, of black cataracts rushing down the steep sides of the Valley. The Liath Macha neighed loudly. The neigh reverberated through the long Valley. A horse neighed joyfully in response. There was a noise of iron doors rushing open somewhere, and a four-footed thunderous trampling on the hollow-sounding earth. A steed came to the Liath Macha. Cuculain felt for his head in the dark, and bitted and bridled him ere he was aware. The horse reared and struggled. The Liath Macha dragged him down the Valley. 'Struggle not, Black Shanglan,' said Cuculain, 'I have tamed thy better.' The horse ceased to struggle. Down and out of the Dark Valley rodest thou, O peerless one, with thy horses. The Liath Macha was grey to whiteness, the other horse was black and glistening like the bright mail of the chaffer. He rode thence to Emain Macha with the two horses like a lord of Day and Night, and of Life and Death. Truly the might and power of the Long-Handed and Far-Shooting one was upon him that night. He came to Emain Macha. The doors of Macha's stable flew open before him. He rode the horses into the stable. Macha's war-car brayed forth a brazen roar of welcome, the Tuatha De Danan shouted, and the car itself glowed and sparkled. The horses went to their ancient stalls, the Liath Macha to that which was nearer to the door. Cuculain took off their bridles and hanged them on the wall. He went forth into the night. The horses were already eating their barley, but they looked after him as he went. The doors shut to with a brazen clash. Cuculain stood alone in the great court under the stars. A druidic storm was abroad and howled in the forests. He thought all that had taken place a wild dream. He went to his dormitory and to his couch. Laeg was asleep with the starlight shining on his white forehead; his red hair was shed over the pillow. Cuculain kissed him, and sitting on the bed's edge wept. Laeg awoke.

'Thou wert not well at supper,' said Laeg, 'and now thou hast been wandering in the damp of the night, and thou with a fever upon thee, for I hear thy teeth clattering. I sought to hinder thee, and thou wouldst not be persuaded. Verily, if thou wilt not again obey me, being thy senior, thou shalt have sore bones at my hands. Undress thyself now and come to bed without delay.'

Cuculain did so.

'Thou art as cold as ice,' said Laeg.

'Nay, I am hotter than fire,' said Cuculain.

'Thou art ice, I say,' said Laeg, 'and thy teeth are clattering like hailstones on a brazen shield. Ay, and thine eyes shine terribly.'

Laeg started from the couch. He struck flintsparks upon a rag steeped in nitre, and waved it to a flame, and kindled a lanthorn. He flung his own mantle upon the bed and went forth in his shirt. The storm raged terribly; the stars were dancing in high heaven. He came to the house of the Chief Leech and beat at the door. The Leech was not in bed. All the wise men of Emain Macha were awake that night, listening to the portents.

'Setanta, son of Sualtam, is sick,' said Laeg.

'What are his symptoms?' said the Leech.

'He is colder than ice, his eyes shine terribly, and his teeth clatter, but he says that he is hotter than fire.'

The Leech went to Cuculain. 'This is not a work for me,' he said, 'but for a seer. Bring hither Cathvah and his Druids.' Cathvah and and his seers came. They made their symbols of power over the youth and chanted their incantations and Druid songs. After that Cuculain slept. He slept for three days and three nights. There was a great stillness while the boy slept, for it was not lawful at any time for anyone to awake Cuculain when he slumbered.

On the third morning Cuculain awoke. The bright morning sunshine was all around, and the birds sang in Emain Macha. He called for Laeg with a loud voice and bade him order a division of the boys to get ready their horses and chariots for charioteering exercise and fighting out of their cars.

XIV

THE KNIGHTING OF CUCULAIN

> 'Then felt I like a watcher of the skies
> When a new planet swims into his ken.'
>
> KEATS.

The prophecies concerning the coming of some extraordinary warrior amongst the Red Branch had been many and ancient, and by certain signs Concobar believed that his time was now near. Often he contemplated his nephew, observed his beauty, his strength, and his unusual proficiency in all martial exercises, and mused deeply considering the omens. But when he saw him slinging and charioteering amongst the rest, shooting spears and casting battle-stones at a mark before the palace upon the lawn, and saw him eating and drinking before him nightly in the hall like another, and heard his clear voice and laughter amongst the boys, his schoolfellows and comrades, then the thought or the faint surmise or wish that his nephew might be that promised one passed out of his mind, for the prophesyings and the rumours had been very great, and men looked for one who should resemble Lu the Long-Handed, son of Ethlend,[52] whose sling was like the cloud bow, who thundered and lightened against the giants of the Fomoroh, who was all power and all skill, whose chain wherewith he used to confine Tuatha De Danan and Milesians, spanned the midnight sky. The rumours and prophecies were indeed exceeding great and Cuculain, though he far surpassed the rest, was but a boy like others. He stood at the head of Concobar's horses when the King ascended his chariot. His shoulder was warm and firm to the touch when the King lightly laid his hand upon him.

One night there were terrible portents. All Ireland quaked; there was a druidic storm under bright stars; the buildings rocked; a brazen clangour sounded from the Tec Brac; there were mighty tramplings and cries and a four-footed thunder of giant hoofs, and they went round Ireland three times, only the third time swifter and like a hurricane of sound. Cuculain was abroad that night. There was deep sleep upon the people of Emain, only the chiefs were awake and aware. Cuculain was sick after that. The Druids stood around his bed.

'The world labours with the new birth,' said Concobar. 'Maybe my nephew is the forerunner, the herald and announcer of the coming god!'

One evening, after supper, when the lad came to bid his uncle good-night as his custom was, he said, 'If it be pleasing to thee, my Uncle Concobar, I would be knighted on the morrow, for I am now of due age, and owing to the instructions of my tutor, Fergus Mac Roy, and thyself, and my other teachers and instructors, I am thought to be sufficiently versed in martial exercises, and able to play a man's part amongst the Red Branch.'

He was now a man's full height, but his face was a boy's face, and his strength and agility amazed all who observed him in his exercises.

'Has thou heard what Cathvah has predicted concerning the youth who is knighted on that day?' said the King.

'Yes,' answered the lad.

'That he will be famous and short-lived and unhappy?'

'Truly,' he replied.

'And doth thy purpose still hold?'

'Yes,' he answered, 'but whether it be mine I cannot tell.'

Concobar, though unwilling, yielded to that request.

Loegairey, the Victorious, son of Conud, son of Iliach, the second best knight of the Red Branch and the most devoted to poetry of them all came that night into the hall while the rest slumbered. The candles were flickering in their sockets. Darkness invested the rest of the vast hollow-sounding chamber, but there was light around the throne and couch of the King, owing to the splendour of the pillars and of the canopy shining with bronze, white and red, and silver and gold, and glittering with carbuncles and diamonds, and owing to the light which always surrounded the King and encircled his regal head like a luminous cloud, seen by many. He was looking straight out before him with bright eyes, considering and consulting for the Red Branch while they slept. Two great men having their swords drawn in their hands, stood behind him, on the right and on the left, like statues, motionless and silent.

Loegairey drew nigh to the King. Distraction and amazement were in his face. His dense and lustrous hair was dishevelled and in agitation round his neck and huge shoulders. He held in his hand two long spears with rings of walrus tooth where the timber met the shank of the flashing blades; they trembled in his hand. His lips were dry, his voice very low.

'There are horses in the stable of Macha,' he said.

'I know it,' answered the King.

Concobar called for water, and when he had washed his hands and his face, he took from its place the chess-board of the realm, arranged the men, and observed their movements and combinations. He closed the board and put the men in their net of bronze wire, and restored all to their place.

'Great things will happen on the morrow, O grandson of Iliach,' he said. 'Take candles and go before me to the boys' dormitory.'

They went to the boys' dormitory and to the couch of Cuculain. Cuculain and Laeg were asleep together there. Their faces towards each other and their hair mingled together. Cuculain's face was very tranquil, and his breathing inaudible, like an infant's.

'O sweet and serene face,' murmured the King, 'I see great clouds of sorrow coming upon you.'

They returned to the hall.

'Go now to thy rest and thy slumber, O Loegairey,' said the King. 'When the curse of Macha descends upon us I know one who will withstand it.'

'Surely it is not that stripling?' said Loegairey. But the King made no answer.

On the morrow there was a great hosting of the Red Branch on the plain of the Assemblies. It was May-Day morning and the sun shone brightly, but at first through radiant showers. The trees were putting forth young buds; the wet grass sparkled. All the martial pomp and glory of the Ultonians were exhibited that day. Their chariots and war-horses ringed the plain. All the horses' heads were turned towards the centre where were Concobar Mac Nessa and the chiefs of the Red Branch. The plain flashed with gold, bronze, and steel, and glowed with the bright mantles of the innumerable heroes, crimson and scarlet, blue, green, or purple. The huge brooches on their breasts of gold and silver or gold-like bronze, were like resplendent wheels. Their long hair, yellow for the most part, was bound with ornaments of gold. Great, truly, were those men, their like has not come since upon the earth. They were the heroes and demigods of the heroic age of Erin, champions who feared nought beneath the sun, mightiest among the mighty, huge, proud, and unconquerable, and loyal and affectionate beyond all others; all of the blood of Ir,[53] son of Milesius, the Clanna Rury of great renown, rejoicing in their valour, their splendour, their fame and their peerless king. Concobar had no crown. A plain circle of beaten gold girt his broad temples. In the naked glory of his regal manhood he stood there before them all, but even so a stranger would have swiftly discovered the captain of the Red Branch, such was his stature, his bearing, such his slowly-turning, steady-gazing eyes and the majesty of his bearded countenance. His countenance was long, broad above and narrow below, his nose eminent, his beard bipartite, curling and auburn in hue, his form without any blemish or imperfection.

Cuculain came forth from the palace. He wore that day a short mantle of pale-red silk bordered with white thread and fastened on the breast with a small brooch like a wheel of silver. The hues upon that silk were never the same. His tunic of fine linen was girt at the waist with a leathern zone, stained to the resemblance of the wild-briar rose. It descended to but did not pass his beautiful knees, falling into many plaits. The tunic was cut low at the neck, exposing his throat and the knot in the throat and the cup-shaped indentation above the breast. On his feet were comely shoes sparkling with bronze plates. They took the colour of everything which they approached. His hair fell in many curls over the pale-red mantle, without adornment or confinement. It

THE KNIGHTING OF CUCULAIN

was the colour of the flower which is named after the dearest Disciple, but which was called sovarchey by the Gael. A tinge of red ran through the gold. As to his eyes, no two men or women could agree concerning their colour, for some said they were blue, and some grey, and others hazel; and there were those who said that they were blacker than the blackest night that was ever known. Yet again, there were those who said that they were of all colours named and nameless. They were soft and liquid splendours, unfathomable lakes of light above his full and ruddy cheeks, and beneath his curved and most tranquil brows. In form he was symmetrical, straight and pliant as a young fir tree when the sweet spring sap fills its veins. So he came to that assembly, in the glory of youth, beauty, strength, valour, and beautiful shame-fastness, yet proud in his humility and glittering like the morning star. Choice youths, his comrades, attended him. The kings held their breaths when he drew nigh, moving white knee after white knee over the green and sparkling grass. When the other rites had been performed and the due sacrifices and libations made, and after Cuculain had put his right hand into the right hand of the King and become his man, Concobar gave him a shield, two spears and a sword, weapons of great price and of thrice proved excellence – a strong man's equipment. Cuculain struck the spears together at right angles and broke them. He clashed the sword flat-wise on the shield. The sword leaped into small pieces and the shield was bent inwards and torn.

'These are not good weapons, my King,' said the boy. Then the King gave him others, larger and stronger and worthy of his best champions. These, too, the boy broke into pieces in like manner.

'Son of Nessa, these are still worse,' he said, 'nor is it well done, O Captain of the Red Branch, to make me a laughing-stock in the presence of this great hosting of the Ultonians.'

Concobar Mac Nessa exulted exceedingly when he beheld the amazing strength and the waywardness of the boy, and beneath delicate brows his eyes glittered like glittering swords as he glanced proudly round on the crowd of martial men that surrounded him. Amongst them all he seemed himself a bright torch of valour and war, more pure and clear than polished steel. He then beckoned to one of his knights, who hastened away and returned bringing Concobar's own shield and spears and sword out of the Tec Brac, where they were kept, an equipment in reserve. And Cuculain shook them and bent them and clashed them together, but they held firm.

'These are good arms, O son of Nessa,' said Cuculain.

'Choose now thy charioteer,' said the King, 'for I will give thee also war-horses and a chariot.'

He caused to pass before Cuculain all the boys who in many and severe tests had proved their proficiency in charioteering, in the management and tending of steeds, in the care of weapons and steed-harness, and all that related to charioteering science. Amongst them was Laeg, with a pale face and dejected, his eyes red and his cheeks stained from much weeping. Cuculain laughed when he saw him, and called him forth from the rest, naming him by his name with a loud, clear voice, heard to the utmost limit of the great host.

'There was fear upon thee,' said Cuculain.

'There is fear upon thyself,' answered Laeg. 'It was in thy mind that I would refuse.'

'Nay, there is no such fear upon me,' said Cuculain.

'Then there is fear upon me,' said Laeg. 'A charioteer needs a champion who is stout and a valiant and faithful. Yea, truly there is fear upon me,' answered Laeg.

'Verily, dear comrade and bed-fellow,' answered Cuculain, 'it is through me that thou shalt get thy death-wound, and I say not this as a vaunt, but as a prophecy.'

And that prophecy was fulfilled, for the spear that slew Laeg went through his master.

After that Laeg stood by Cuculain's side and held his peace, but his face shone with excess of joy and pride. He wore a light graceful frock of deerskin, joined in the front with a twine of bronze wire, and a short, dark-red cape, secured by a pin of gold with a ring to it. A band of gold thread confined his auburn hair, rising into a peak behind his head. In his hands he held a goad of polished red-yew, furnished with a crooked hand-grip of gold, and pointed with shining bronze, and where the bronze met the timber there was a circlet of diamond of the diamonds of Banba. He had also a short-handled scourge with a haft of walrus tooth, and the rope, cord, and lash of that scourge were made of delicate and delicately-twisted thread of copper. This equipment was the equipment of a proved charioteer; the apprentices wore only grey capes with white fringes, fastened by loops of red cord.

Laeg was one of three brothers, all famous charioteers. Id and Sheeling were the others. They were all three sons of the King of Gabra, whose bright dun arose upon a green and sloping hill over against Tara towards the rising of the sun. Thence sprang the beautiful stream of the Nemnich, rich in lilies and reeds and bulrushes, which to-day men call the Nanny Water. Laeg was grey-eyed and freckled.

Then there were led forward by two strong knights a pair of great and spirited horses and a splendid war-car. The King said, 'They are thine, dear nephew. Well I know that neither thou, nor Laeg, will be a dishonour to this war equipage.'

Cuculain sprang into the car, and standing with legs apart, he stamped from side to side and shook the car mightily, till the axle brake, and the car itself was broken in pieces.

'It is not a good chariot,' said the lad.

Another was led forward, and he broke it in like manner.

'Give me a sound chariot, High Lord of the Clanna Rury, or give me none,' he said. 'No prudent warrior would fight from such brittle foothold.'

He brake in succession nine war chariots, the greatest and strongest in Emain. When he broke the ninth the horses of Macha neighed from their stable. Great fear fell upon the host when they heard that unusual noise and the reverberation of it in the woods and hills.

'Let those horses be harnessed to the Chariot of Macha,' cried Concobar, 'and let Laeg, son of the King of Gabra, drive them hither, for those are the horses and that the chariot which shall be given this day to Cuculain.'

Then, son of Sualtam, how in thy guileless breast thy heart leaped, when thou heardest the thundering of the great war-car and the wild neighing of the immortal steeds, as they broke from the dark stable into the clear-shining light of day, and heard behind them the ancient roaring of the brazen wheels as in the days when they bore forth Macha and her martial groom against the giants of old, and mightily established in Eiriu the Red Branch of the Ultonians! Soon they rushed to view from the rear of Emain, speeding forth impetuously out of the hollow-sounding ways of the city and the echoing palaces into the open, and behind them in the great car green and gold, above the many-twinkling wheels, the charioteer, with floating mantle, girt round the temples with the gold fillet of his office, leaning backwards and sideways as he laboured to restrain their fury unrestrainable; a grey long-maned steed, whale-bellied, broad-chested, with mane like flying foam, under one silver yoke, and a black lustrous, tufty-maned steed under the other, such steeds as in power, size, and beauty the earth never produced before and never will produce again.

Like a hawk swooping along the face of a cliff when the wind is high, or like the rush of March wind over the smooth plain, or like the fleetness of the stag roused from his lair by the hounds and covering his first field, was the rush of those steeds when they had broken through the restraint of the charioteer, as though they galloped over fiery flags, so that the earth shook and trembled with the velocity of their motion, and all the time the great car brayed and shrieked as the wheels of solid and glittering bronze went round, and strange cries and exclamations were heard, for they were demons that had their abode in that car.

The charioteer restrained the steeds before the assembly, but nay-the-less a deep purr, like the purr of a tiger, proceeded from the axle. Then the whole assembly lifted up their voices and shouted for Cuculain, and he himself, Cuculain, the son of Sualtam, sprang into his chariot, all armed, with a cry as of a warrior springing into his chariot in the battle, and he stood erect and brandished his spears, and the war sprites of the Gael shouted along with him, for the Bocanahs and Bananahs and the Geniti Glindi, the wild people of the glens, and the demons of the air, roared around him, when first the great warrior of the Gael, his battle-arms in his hands, stood equipped for war in his chariot before all the warriors of his tribe, the kings of the Clanna Rury and the people of Emain Macha. Then, too, there

THE KNIGHTING OF CUCULAIN

sounded from the Tec Brac the boom of shields, and the clashing of swords and the cries and shouting of the Tuatha De Danan, who dwelt there perpetually; and Lu the Long-Handed, the slayer of Balor, the destroyer of the Fomoroh, the immortal, the invisible, the maker and decorator of the Firmament, whose hound was the sun and whose son the viewless wind, thundered from heaven and bent his sling five-hued against the clouds; and the son of the illimitable Lir[54] in his mantle blue and green, foam-fringed passed through the assembly with a roar of far-off innumerable waters, and the Mor Reega stood in the midst with a foot on either side of the plain, and shouted with the shout of a host, so that the Ultonians fell down like reaped grass with their faces to the earth, on account of the presence of the Mor Reega, and on account of the omens and great signs.

Cuculain bade Laeg let the steeds go. They went like a storm and three times encircled Emain Macha. It was the custom of the Ultonians to march thrice round Emain ere they went forth to war.

Then said Cuculain – 'Whither leads the great road yonder?'

'To Ath-na-Forairey and the borders of the Crave Rue.'

'And wherefore is it called the Ford of the Watchings?' said Cuculain.

'Because,' answered Laeg, 'there is always one of the King's knights there, keeping watch and ward over the gate of the province.'

'Guide thither the horses,' said Cuculain, 'for I will not lay aside my arms till I have first reddened them in the blood of the enemies of my nation. Who is it that is over the ward there this day?'

'It is Conall Carnach,' said Laeg.

As they drew nigh to the ford, the watchman from his high watch-tower on the west side of the dun sent forth a loud and clear voice –

'There is a chariot coming to us from Emain Macha,' he said. 'The chariot is of great size; I have not seen its like in all Eiriu. In front of it are two horses, one black and one white. Great is their trampling and their glory and the shaking of their heads and necks. I liken their progress to the fall of water from a high cliff or the sweeping of dust and beech-tree leaves over a plain, when the March wind blows hard, or to the rapidity of thunder rattling over the firmament. A man would say that there were eight legs under each horse, so rapid and indistinguishable is the motion of their limbs and hoofs. Identify those horses, O Conall, and that chariot, for to me they are unknown.'

'And to me likewise,' said Conall. 'Who are in the chariot? Moderate, O man, the extravagance of thy language, for thou art not a prophet but a watchman.'

'There are two beardless youths in the chariot,' answered the watchman, 'but I am unable to identify them on account of the dust and the rapid motion and the steam of the horses. I think the charioteer is Laeg, the son of the King of Gabra, for I know his manner of driving. The boy who sits in front of him and below him on the champion's seat I do not know, but he shines like a star in the cloud of dust and steam.'

Then a young man who stood near to Conall Carna, wearing a short, red cloak with a blue hood to it, and a tassel at the point of the hood, said to Conall –

'If it be my brother that charioteers sure am I that it is Cuculain who is in the fighter's seat, for many a time have I heard Laeg utter foul scorn of the Red Branch, none excepted, when compared with Sualtam's son. For no other than him would he deign to charioteer. Truly though he is my own brother there is not such a boaster in the North.'

Then the watchman cried out again –

'Yea, the charioteer is the son of the King of Gabra, and it is Cuculain, the son of Sualtam, who sits in the fighter's seat. He has Concobar's own shield on his breast, and his two spears in his hand. Over Bray Ros, over Brainia, they are coming along the highway, by the foot of the Town of the Tree; it is gifted with victories.'

'Have done, O talkative man,' cried Conall, 'whose words are like the words of a seer, or the full-voiced intonement of a chief bard.'

When the chariot came to the ford, Conall was amazed at the horses and the chariot, but he dissembled his amazement before his people, and when he saw Cuculain armed, he laughed and said, –

'Hath the boy indeed taken arms?'

And Cuculain said, 'It is as thou seest, O son of Amargin; and moreover, I have sworn not to let them back into the Chamber-of-Many-Colours[55] until I shall have first reddened them in the blood of the enemies of Ulla.'

THE KNIGHTING OF CUCULAIN

Then Conall ceased laughing and said, 'Not so, Setanta, for verily thou shalt not be permitted;' and the great Champion sprang forward to lay his fearless, never-foiled, and all conquering hands on the bridles of the horses, but at a nod from Cuculain, Laeg let the steeds go, and Conall sprang aside out of the way, so terrible was the appearance of the horses as they reared against him. 'Harness my horses and yoke my chariot,' cried Conall, 'for if this mad boy goes into the enemies' country and meets with harm there, verily I shall never be forgiven by the Ultonians.'

His horses were harnessed and his chariot yoked, – illustrious too were those horses, named and famed in many songs – and Conall and Ide in their chariot dashed through the ford enveloped with rainbow-painted clouds of foam and spray, and like hawks on the wing they skimmed the plain, pursuing the boys. Laeg heard the roar and trampling, and looking back over his shoulder, said, –

'They are after us, dear master, namely the great son of Amargin and my haughty brother Ide, who hath ever borne himself to me as though I were a wayward child. They would spoil upon us this our brave foray. But they will overtake the wind sooner than they will overtake the Liath Macha and Black Shanglan, whose going truly is like the going of eagles. O storm-footed steeds, great is my love for you, and inexpressible my pride in your might and your beauty, your speed and your terror, and sweet docility and affection.'

'Nevertheless, O Laeg,' said Cuculain, 'slacken now their going, for that Champion will be an impediment to us in our challengings and our fightings; for when we stop for that purpose he will overtake us, and, be our feats what they may, his and not ours will be the glory. Slacken the going of the horses, for we must rid ourselves of the annoyance and the pursuit of these gadflies.'

Laeg slackened the pace, and as they went Cuculain leaped lightly from his seat and as lightly bounded back again, holding a great pebble in his hand, such as a man using all his strength could with difficulty raise from the ground, and sat still, rejoicing in his purpose, and grasping the pebble with his five fingers.

Conall and Ide came up to them after that, and Conall, as the senior and the best man amongst the Ultonians, clamorously called to them to turn back straightway, or he would hough their horses, or draw the linch-pins of their wheels, or in some other manner bring their foray to naught. Cuculain thereupon stood upright in the car, and so standing, with feet apart to steady him in his throwing and in his aim, dashed the stone upon the yoke of Conall's chariot between the heads of the horses and broke the yoke, so that the pole fell to the ground and the chariot tilted forward violently. Then the charioteer fell amongst the horses, and Conall Carna, the beauty of the Ultonians the battle-winning and ever-victorious son of Amargin, was shot out in front upon the road, and fell there upon his left shoulder, and his beautiful raiment was defiled with dust; and when he arose his left hand hung by his side, for the shoulder-bone was driven from the socket, owing to the violence of the fall.

'I swear by all my gods,' he cried, 'that if a step would save thy head from the hands of the men of Meath, I would not take it.'

Cuculain laughed and replied, 'Good, O Conall, and who asked thee to take it, or craved of thee any succour or countenance? Was it a straight shot? Are there the materials of a fighter in me at all, dost thou think? Thou art in my debt now too, O Conall. I have saved thee a broken vow, for it is one of the oaths of our Order not to enter hostile territory with brittle chariot-gear!'

Then the boys laughed at him again, and Laeg let go the steeds, and very soon they were out of sight. Conall returned slowly with his broken chariot to Ath-na-Forairey and sent for Fingin of Slieve Fuad, who was the most cunning physician and most expert of bone-setters amongst the Ultonians. Conall's messengers experienced no difficulty in finding the house of the leech, which was very recognisable on account of its shape and appearance, and because it had wide open doors, four in number, affording a liberal ingress and free thoroughfare to all the winds. Also a stream of pure water ran through the house, derived from a well of healing properties, which sprang from the side of the uninhabited hill. Such were the signs that showed the house of a leech.

When they drew nigh they heard the voice of one man talking and of another who laughed. It happened that that day there had been borne thither a champion, in whose body there was not one small bone unbroken or uninjured. The man's bruises and fractures had been dressed and set by Fingin and his intelligent and deft-handed apprentices, and he lay now in his bed of healing listening joyfully to the conversation of the leech, who was beyond all others eloquent and of most agreeable discourse.

When Conall's messengers related the reason of their coming, Fingin cried to his young men, 'Harness me my horses and yoke my chariot. There are few,' he said, 'in Erin for whom I would leave my own house, but that youth is one of them. His father Amargin was well known to me. He was a warrior grim and dour exceedingly, and he ever said concerning the boy, "This hound's whelp that I have gotten is too fine and sleek to hold bloody gaps or hunt down a noble prey. He will be a women's playmate and not a peer amongst Heroes." And that fear was ever upon him till the day when Conall came red out of the Valley of the Thrush, and his track thence to Rath-Amargin was one straight path of blood, and he with his shield-arm hacked to the bone, his sword-arm swollen and bursting, and the flame of his valour burning bright in his splendid eyes. Then, for the first time, the old man smiled upon him, and he said, "That arm, my son, has done a man's work to-day."'

XV

ACROSS THE MEARINGS AND AWAY

'Say, rushed the bold eagle exultingly forth.
From his home, in the dark rolling clouds of the North?'
CAMPBELL.

As for the boys, they proceeded joyfully after that pleasant skirmish and friendly encounter, both on account of the discomfiture of him who was reckoned the prime champion of the Ultonians, and because they were at large in Erin, with no one to direct them, or to whom they should render an account; and their happiness, too, was increased by the mettle, power and gallant action of the steeds, and by the clanking of the harness and the brazen chains, and the ringing of the weapons of war, and the roar of the revolving wheels, and owing to the velocity of their motion and the rushing of the wind upon their temples and through their hair.

Then Cuculain stood up in the chariot, and surveyed the land on all sides, and said –

'What is that great, firm-based, indestructible mountain upon our left hand, one of a noble range which, rising from the green plain, runs eastward. The last peak there is the mountain of which I speak, whose foot is in the Ictian sea and whose head neighbours the firmament.'

And Laeg said, 'Men call it Slieve Modurn, after a giant of the elder time, when men were mightier and greater than they are now. He was of the children of Brogan, uncle of Milesius, and his brothers were Fuad and Eadar and Breagh, and all these being very great men are commemorated in the names of noble mountains and sea-dividing promontories.'

'Guide thither the horses,' said Cuculain. 'It is right that those who take the road against an enemy should first spy out the land, choosing judiciously their point of onset, and Slieve Modurn yonder commands a most brave prospect.'

Laeg did so. There, in a green valley, they unharnessed the horses and tethered them to graze, and they themselves climbed the mountain and stood upon the top in the most clear air. Thence Laeg showed him the green plain of Meath extending far and wide, and the great streams of Meath where they ran, the Boyne and the Blackwater, the Liffey and the Royal Rye, and his own stream the Nanny Water, clear and sparkling, which was very dear to Laeg, because he had snared fish there and erected dams, and had done divers boyish feats upon its shores.

Cuculain said, 'I see a beautiful green hill, shaped like an inverted ewer, on the south shore of the Boyne. There is a noble palace there. I see the flashing of its lime-white sides, and the colours of the variegated roof and around it are other beautiful houses. How is that city named O Laeg, and who dwells there?'

'That is the hill of Temair,' answered Laeg, 'Tara's high citadel. Well may that city be beautiful, for the seat of Erin's high sovereignty is there. The man who holds it is Arch-king of all Erin.'

'Westward by south,' said Cuculain, 'I see another city widely built, and unenclosed by ramparts and defensive works, and hard by there is a most smooth plain. At one end of the plain I see a glittering, and also at the other.'

And Laeg said, 'That is the hill of Talteen, so named because the mother of far-shooting Lu, the Deliverer, is worshipped there, and every year, when the leaves change their colour, games and contests of skill are celebrated there in her honour. So it was enjoined on the men of Erin by her famous son. Chariot races are run there on that smooth plain. The glittering points on either side of it are the racing pillars of burnished brass, the starting-post, and that which the charioteers graze with the glowing axle. Many a noble chariot has been broken, and many a gallant youth slain at the further of those twain. It was there that Concobar raced his steeds against the woman with child, concerning which things there are rumours and prophesyings.'

So Cuculain questioned Laeg concerning the cities of Meath, and concerning the noble raths and duns where the kings and lords and chief men of Meath dwelt prosperously, rejoicing in their great wealth. Cuculain said, 'None of these kings and lords and chief men whom thou hast enumerated have at any time injured my nation, and there is not one upon whom I might rightly take vengeance. But I see one other splendid dun, and of this thou hast said no word, though thrice I have questioned thee concerning it.'

Laeg grew pale at these words, and he said,

'What dun is that, my master?'

Cuculain said, 'O fox that thou art, right well thou knowest. It is not a little or mean one, but great, proud, and conspicuous, and vauntingly it rears its head like a man who has never known defeat, but on the contrary has caused many widows to lament. Its white sides flashed against the dark waters of the Boyne, and its bright roofs glitter above the green woods. There is a stream that runs into the Boyne beside it, and there are bulwarks around it, and great strong barriers.'

Laeg answered, 'That is the dun of the sons of Nectan.'

'Let us now leave Slieve Modurn,' said Cuculain, 'and guide thither my horses, for I shall lay waste that dun, and burn it with fire, after having slain the men who dwell there.'

Then Laeg clasped his comrade's knees, and said, 'Take the road, dear master, against the royalest dun in all Meath, but pass by that dun. The men are not alive to-day who at any time approached it with warlike intent. Those who dwell there are sorcerers and enchanters, lords of all the arts of poison and of war.'

Cuculain answered, 'I swear by my gods that Dun-Mic-Nectan is the only dun in all Meath which shall hear my warlike challenge this day. Descend the hill now, for verily thither shalt thou fare, and that whether thou art willing or unwilling.'

Now, for the first time, his valour and his destructive wrath were kindled in the soul of Dethcaen's nursling. Laeg saw the tokens of it, and feared and obeyed. Unwillingly he came down the slopes of Slieve Modurn, and unwillingly harnessed the horses and yoked the chariot, and yoked the horses. Southwards, then, they fared swiftly through the night, and the intervening nations heard them as they went. When they arrived at the dun of the sons of Nectan it was twilight and the dawning of the day. Before the dun there was a green and spacious lawn in full view of the palace, and on the lawn a pillar and on the pillar a huge disc of shining bronze. Cuculain descended and examined the disc, and there was inscribed on it in *ogham* a curse upon the man who should enter that lawn and depart again without battle and single combat with the men of the dun. Cuculain took the disc from its place and cast it from him southwards. The brazen disc skimmed low across the plain and then soared on high until it showed to those who looked a full, bright face, like the moon's, after which, pausing one moment, it fell sheer down and sank into the dark waters of the Boyne, without a sound, or at all disturbing the tranquil surface of the great stream, and was no more seen.

'That bright lure,' said Cuculain, 'shall no more be a cause of death to brave men. This lawn, O Laeg, is surely the richest of all the lawns in the world. Close-enwoven and thick is the mantle of short green grass which it wears, decked all over with red-petalled daisies and bright flowers more numerous than the stars on a frosty night.'

'That is not surprising,' said Laeg, 'for the lawn is enriched and made fat by the blood that has been shed abundantly now for a long time, the blood of heroes and valiant men – slain here by the people of the dun. Very rich too, are the men, both on account of their strippings of the slain, and on account of the druidic well of magic which is within the dun. For the people come from far and near to pay their vows at that well, and they give costly presents to those sorcerers who are priests and custodians of the same.'

'Noble, indeed, is the dun,' said Cuculain. 'But it is yet early, for the sun is not yet risen from his red-flaming eastern couch, and the people of the dun, too, are in their heavy slumber. I would repose now for a while and rest myself before the battles and hard combats which await me this day. Wherefore, good Laeg, let down the sides and seats of the chariot, that I may repose myself for a little and take a short sleep.'

For just then precisely an unwonted drowsiness and desire for slumber possessed Cuculain.

'Witless and devoid of sense art thou,' answered Laeg, 'for who but an idiot would think of sweet sleep and agreeable repose in a hostile territory, much more in full view of those who look out from a foeman's dun, and that dun, Dun-Mic-Nectan?'

'Do as I bid thee,' said Cuculain. 'For one day, if for no other, thou shalt obey my commands.'

Laeg unyoked the chariot and turned the great steeds forth to graze on the druidic lawn, which was never done before at any time. He let down the chariot and arranged it as a couch, and his young master laid himself therein, composing his limbs and pillowing tranquilly his head, and he closed his immortal eyes. Very soon sweet slumber possessed him. Laeg meanwhile kept watch and ward, and his great heart in his breast continually trembled like the leaf of the poplar tree, or like a rush in a flooded stream. The awakening birds unconscious sang in the trees, the dew glittered on the grass; hard by the royal Boyne rolled silently. The son of Sualtam slumbered without sound or motion, and the charioteer stood beside him upright, like a pillar, his grey bright eyes fixed upon the house of the sorcerers, the merciless, bloody, and ever-victorious sons of Nectan, the son of Labrad.

Of the people of the dun, Foil, son of Nectan, was the first to awake. It was his custom to wander forth by himself early in the morning, devising snares and stratagems by which he might take and destroy men at his leisure. He was more cruel than anything. By him the great door of the dun, bound and rivetted with brass, was flung open. With one hand he backshot the bar, which rushed into its chamber with a roar and crash as of a great house when it falls, and with the other he drew back the door. It grated on its brazen hinges, and on the iron threshold, with a noise like thunder. Then Foil stood black and huge in the wide doorway of the dun, and he looked at Laeg and Laeg looked at him. The man was ugly and fierce of aspect. His hair was thick and black; he was bull-necked and large-eared. His mantle was black, bordered with dark red; his tunic, a dirty yellow, was splashed with recent blood. There were great shoes on his feet soled with wood and iron. In his hand he bore a staff of quick-beam, as it were a full-grown tree without its branches. He being thus, strode forward in an ungainly manner to Laeg, and with a surly voice bade him drive the horses off the lawn.

'Drive them off thyself,' said Laeg.

He sought to do that, but owing to the behaviour of the steeds, he desisted right soon, and turned again to Laeg.

'Who is the sleeping youth?' said he, 'and wherefore hath he come hither in an evil hour?'

'He is a certain mild and gentle youth of the Ultonians,' replied Laeg, 'who yester morning prosperously assumed his arms of chivalry for the first time, and hath come hither to prove his valour upon the sons of Nectan.'

'Many youths of his nation have come hither with the same intent,' said the giant, 'but they did not return.'

'This youth will,' said Laeg, 'after having slain the sons of Nectan, and after having sacked their dun and burned it with fire.'

Foil hearing that word became very angry, and he gripped his great staff and advanced to make a sudden end of Laeg first, and then of the sleeper, Laeg, on his side, drew Cuculain's sword. Hardly and using all his strength, could he do so and at the same time hold himself in an attitude of defence and attack, but he succeeded. His aspect, too, was high and warlike, and his eyes shone menacingly the while his heart trembled, for he knew too well that he was no match for the man.

'Go back now for thy weapons of war,' he cried, 'and all thy war-furniture, and thy instruments of sorcery and enchantment. Truly thou art in need of them all.'

When Foil saw how the enormous sword flashed in the lad's hand, and saw the fierceness of his visage and heard his menacing words, he returned to the dun. The people of the dun were now awake, and they clustered like bees on the slope of the mound, and in the covered ways beneath the eaves and along the rampart, and they hissed and roared and shouted words of insult and contumely, lewd and gross, concerning

Laeg and concerning that other youth who slept in such a place and at such a time. But Laeg stood still and silent, with his eyes fixed on the dun, and with the point of his sword leaning on the ground, for his right hand was weary on account of its great weight. Very ardently he longed that his master should awake out of that unreasonable slumber. Yet he made no attempt to rouse him, for it was unlawful to awake Cuculain when he slept. Conspicuous amongst the people of the dun were Foil's brethren, Tuatha and Fenla, Tuatha vast in bulk, and Fenla, tall and swift, wearing a mantle of pale blue. Around Fenla stood the three cup-bearers, who drew water from the magic well, Flesc, Lesc, and Leam were their names. At the same time that Foil reappeared in the doorway of the dun, fully armed and equipped for battle, Cuculain awoke and sat up. At first he was dazed and bewildered, for divine voices were sounding in his ears, and fleeting visionary presences were departing from him. Then he heard the people how they shouted and saw his enemy descending the slope of the dun, sights and sounds indeed diverse from those his dreams and visions. With a cry he started from his bed, like a deer starting from his lair, and the people of the dun fell suddenly silent when they beheld the velocity of his movements, the splendour of his beauty, and the rapidity with which he armed himself and stood forth for war.

'That champion is Foil, son of Nectan,' said Laeg, 'and there is not one in the world with whom it is more difficult to contend both in other respects and chiefly in this, that there is but one weapon wherewith he may be slain. To all others he is invulnerable. That weapon is an iron ball having magic properties, and no man knows where to look for it, or where the man hath hidden it away. And O my dear master, thou goest forth to certain death going forth against that man.'

'Have no fear on that account,' said Cuculain, 'for it has been revealed to me where he hides it. It is a ges to him to wear it always on his breast above his armour, but beneath his mantle and tunic. There it is suspended by a strong chain of brass around his neck. With that ball I shall slay him in the manner in which I have been directed by those who visited me while I slept.'

Then they fought, and in the first close so vehement was the onset of Foil, that Cuculain could do no more than defend himself, and around the twain sparks flew up in showers as from a smithy where a blacksmith and his lusty apprentices strongly beat out the red iron. The second was similar to the first, and equally without results. In the third close Cuculain, having sheathed his sword, sprang upwards and dashed his shield into the giant's face, and at the same time he tore from its place of concealment the magic ball, rending mightily the brazen chain. And he leaped backwards, and taking a swift aim, threw. The ball flew from the young hero's hand like a bolt from a sling, and it struck the giant in the middle of the forehead below the rim of his helmet, but above his blazing eyes, and the ball crashed through the strong frontal bone, and tore its way through the hinder part of his head, and went forth, carrying the brains with it in its course, so that there was a free tunnel and thoroughfare for all the winds of heaven there. With a crash and a ringing, armour and weapons, the giant fell upon the plain and his blood poured forth in a torrent there where he himself invulnerable had shed the blood of so many heroes. Laeg rejoiced greatly at that feat, and with a loud voice bade the men of the dun bring forth their next champion. This was Tuatha the second son of Nectan, and the fiercest of the three, he buffeted his esquires and *gillas*, while they armed him, so that it was a sore task for them to clasp and strap and brace his armour upon him that day, for their faces were bloody from his hands, and the floor of the armoury was strewn with their teeth. That armour was a marvel and astonishment to all who saw it, so many thick, hard skins of wild oxen of the mountains had been stitched together to furnish forth the champion's coat of mail. It was strengthened, too, with countless bars and rings of brass sewed fast to it all over, and it encompassed the whole of his mighty frame, from his shoulders to his feet. The helmet and neckpiece were one, wrought in like manner, only stronger. The helmet covered his face. There was no opening there save breathing slits and two round holes through which his eyes shone terribly. On his feet were strong shoes bound with brass. To any other man but himself this armour would have been an encumbrance, for it was good and sufficient loading for a car drawn by one yoke of oxen; but so clad, this man was aware of no unusual weight. When they had clasped him and braced him to his satisfaction, and, indeed, that was not easy, they put upon him his tunic of dusky grey, and over that his mantle of dark crimson, and fastened it on his breast with a brooch whose wheel alone would task one man's full strength to lift from the ground.

Then Tuatha went forth out of the dun, and when his people saw him they shouted mightily, for before that they had been greatly dismayed, and cast down on account of the slaying of Foil, whom till then they had deemed invincible. They were all males dwelling here together in sorcery and common lust for blood. No woman brightened their dark assemblies and the voice of a child was never heard within the dun or around it. So they rejoiced greatly when they beheld Tuatha and saw him how wrathfully he came forth, breathing slaughter, and heard his voice; for terribly he shouted as he strode down from the dun, and he banned and cursed Cuculain and Laeg, and devoted them to his gloomy gods. Beneath his feet the massive timbers of the drawbridge bent and creaked.

Said Laeg, 'This man, O dear Setanta, is far more terrible than the first, for he is said to be altogether invulnerable and proof against any weapon that was ever made.'

'It is not altogether thus,' said Cuculain, 'but if the man escapes the first stroke he is thenceforward invincible, and surely slays his foe. Therefore give into my hand Concobar's unendurable and mighty ashen spear, for I must make an end of him at one cast or not at all.'

Tuatha now rushed upon Cuculain, flinging darts, of which he carried many in his left hand. Not one of them did Cuculain attempt to take upon his shield, but altogether eluded them, for now he swerved to one side and now to another, and now he dropped on one knee and again sprang high in air, so that the missile hurtled and hissed between his gathered feet. Truly since the beginning of the world there was not, and to the end of the world there will not be, a better leaper than thy nursling, daughter of Cathvah; and behind him all the lawn was as it were sown thick with spears, and these so buried in the earth that two-thirds of their length was concealed and a third only projected slantwise from the green and glittering sward. When the man with all his force, fury, and venom had discharged his last shaft and seen it, too, shoot screaming beneath the aerial feet of the hero, he roared so terribly that the shores and waters of the Boyne and the surrounding woods and groves returned a hollow moan, and, laying his right hand on the hand-grip of his sword, he rushed upon Cuculain. At that moment Cuculain poised the broad-bladed spear of Concobar Mac Nessa and cast it at the man, who was now very near, and came rushing on like a storm, having his vast sword drawn and flashing. That cast no one could rightly blame whether as to force or direction, for the brazen blade caught the son of Nectan full on breast under the left pap and tore through his thick and strong armour and burst three rib bones, and fixed itself in his heart, so that he fell first upon his knees, stumbling forward, and then rolled over on the plain and a torrent of black blood gushed from his mouth and nostrils.

'That was indeed a brave cast,' said Laeg, 'for the coat is the thickness of seven bulls' hides, and plated besides, and the rib-bones, through which Concobar's great spear impelled by thee hath burst his victorious way, are stronger than the thigh-bones of a horse; but pluck out the spear now, for it is beyond my power to do so, and stand well upon thy guard, for the two combats past will be as child's play to that which now awaits thee. Fenla, the third son of Nectan, is preparing himself for battle. He is called the Swallow, because there is not a man in the world swifter to retreat, or swifter to pursue. He is more at home in the water than on the dry land, for through it he dives like a water-dog, and glides like an eel, and rushes like a salmon when in the spring-time he seeks the upper pools. Greatly I fear that his challenge and defiance will be to do battle with him there, where no man born of woman can meet him and live.'

'Say not so, O Laeg,' said Cuculain, 'and be not so afraid and cast down, but still keep a cheerful heart in thy breast and a high and brave countenance before the people of the dun. For my tutor Fergus paid a good heed to my education in the whole art of war and especially as to swimming. He is himself a most noble swimmer and I have profited by his instructions. Once he put me to the test. It was in the great swimming bath in the Callan, dug out, it is said, by the Firbolgs in the ancient days, and the trial was in secret and its issue has not been revealed to this day. On that occasion I swam round the bath holding two well-grown boys in my right arm and two in my left, and there was a fifth sitting on my shoulders with his hands clasped on my forehead, and my back was not wetted by the Callan. Therefore dismiss thy fear and answer thou their challenge with a strong voice and a cheerful countenance.'

Laeg did that and he answered their challenge with a voice that rang, striking fear into the hearts of those who heard him. Forthwith, then, Fenla, wearing sword and shield, sprang at a bound over the rampart and foss, and his course thence to the Boyne was like a flash of blue and white and he plunged into the dark stream like a bright spear, and diving beneath the flood he emerged a great way off, and cried aloud for his foe.

'I am here,' cried Cuculain, at his side. 'Cease thy shouting and look to thyself, for it is not my custom to take advantage of any man.'

Marvellous and terrible was the battle which then ensued between these champions. For the spray and the froth and the flying spume of the convulsed and agitated waters around that warring twain, rose in white clouds, and owing to the fierceness of the combat and the displacement of the waters around them, the Boyne on either hand beat her green margin with sudden and unusual billows, for the divine river was taken with a great surprise on that occasion. Amid the roar of the waters ever sounded the dry clash of the meeting swords and the clang of the smitten shields and the ringing of helmets. Sometimes one champion would dive seeking an advantage, and the other would dive too, in order to elude or meet the assault. Then the frothing surface of the stream would clear itself, and the Boyne run dark as before, though the mounted water showed that the combat still raged in its depths. The swallows, too, had been scared away, returning, skimmed the surface, and the bird which is the most beautiful of all darted a bright streak low across the dark water. Anon the submerged champions, coming to the surface for breath, renewed their deadly combat amid foaming waters and clouds of spray. The full particulars of this combat are not related, only that the wizard-champion grew weaker, while his vigour and strength continued unabated with the son of Sualtam, and that in the end he slew the other, and in the sight of all he cut off his head and flung it from the middle Boyne to the shore, and that the headless trunk of Fenla, son of Nectan, floated down-stream to the sea. When the people of the dun saw that, they brake forth west-ward and fled. Then Cuculain and Laeg invaded the dun, and they burst open the doors of the strong chambers, and of the dungeons beneath the earth, and let loose the prisoners and the hostages and the prepared victims, and they broke the idols and the instruments of sorcery, and filled in the well. After that they replenished the vacant places of the war-car with things the most precious and such as were portable, and gave all the rest to the liberated captives for a prey. Last of all they applied fire to the vast dun, and quickly the devouring flames shot heavenward, fed with pine and red yew, and rolled forth a mighty pillar of black smoke, reddened with rushing sparks and flaming embers. The men of Tara saw it, and the men of Tlatga, and of Tailteen, and of Ben-Eadar, and they consulted their prophets and wizards as to what this portent might mean, for it was not a little smoke that the burning of Dun-Mic-Nectan sent forth that day.

XVI

THE RETURN OF CUCULAIN

'The golden gates of sleep unbar
When strength and beauty met together
Kindle their image like a star
In a sea of glassy weather.'

                                             SHELLEY.

Then Laeg harnessed the horses and yoked the chariot. To the brazen peaks of the chariot he fastened the heads of Foil and of Tuatha, with Foil's on the left hand and Tuatha's on the right; and the long-haired head of the water-wizard he made fast by its own hair to the ornament of silver that was at the forward extremity of the great chariot pole. When this was done, and when he had secured his master's weapons and warlike equipments in their respective places, the youths ascended the chariot, and Laeg shook the ringing reins and called to the steeds to go, and they went, and soon they were on the hard highway straining forward to the north. The sound of the war-car behind them outroared the roaring of the flames. Cuculain was a pale red all over, for ere the last combat was at an end that pool of the Boyne was like one bath of blood. His eyes blazed terribly in his head, and his face was fearful to look upon. Like a reed in a river so he quaked and trembled, and there went out from him a moaning like the moaning of winds through deep woods or desolate glens, or over the waste places of the earth when darkness is abroad.

For the war-fury which the Northmen named after the Barserkers enwrapped and inflamed him, body and spirit, owing to those strenuous combats, and owing to the venom and the poison which exhaled from those children of sorcery, that spawn of Death and Hell, so that his gentle mind became as it were the meeting-place of storms and the confluence of shouting seas. A man ran before him whose *bratta* on the wind roared like fire, and there was a sound of voices calling and acclaiming, and a noontide darkness descended upon him and accompanied him as he went, and all became obscure and shapeless, and all the ways were murk. And the mind of Laeg, too, was disturbed and shaken loose from its strong foundations.

'But now,' said Cuculain, 'there ran a man before us. Him I do not see, but what is this herd of monstrous deer, sad-coloured and livid, as with horns and hoofs of iron? I have not seen such at any time. Lurid fire plays round them as they flee.'

'No deer of the earth are they,' said Laeg. 'They are the enchanted herd of Slieve Fuad, and from their abode subterrene they have come up late into the world surrounded by night that they may graze upon Eiriu's plains, and it is not lawful even to look upon them.'

'Pursue and run down those deer,' said Cuculain.

'There is fear upon me,' said Laeg.

'Alive or dead thou shalt come with me on this adventure, though it lead us into the mighty realms of the dead,' cried Cuculain.

Laeg relaxed his hands upon the reins and let the steeds go, and they chased the enchanted herd of Slieve Fuad. There was no hunting seen like that before in Erin. So vehement was the chase that a twain of the herd was run down and they upon their knees and sobbing. Cuculain sprang from the chariot and he made fast one of the deer to the pole of the chariot to run before, and on to the hinder part of it to run behind. So they went northward again with a deer of the herd of Hell running before them and another following behind.

'What are those birds whiter than snow and more brilliant than stars,' said then Cuculain, 'which are before us upon the plain, as if Heaven with its astral lights and splendour were outspread before us there?'

'They are the wild geese of the enchanted flocks of Lir,' answered Laeg. 'From his vast and ever-during realms beneath the sea they have come up through the dim night to feed on Banba's plains. Have nought to do with those birds, dear master.'

Cuculain stood up in his chariot with his sling in his hand, and he fitted thereto small bolts, and slang. He did not make an end before he had overthrown and laid low three score of the birds of Lir.

'Go bring me those birds,' said he to Laeg. The horses were plunging terribly when he said that.

'I may not, O my master,' said Laeg. 'For even now, and with the reins in my hand, I am unable to restrain their fury and their madness, to such a degree have their noble minds been disturbed by the sorcery and the druidism and the enchantment with which they are surrounded. And I fear that soon the brazen wheels will fail me, or that the axle-tree will fail me by reason of their collidings with the rocks and cliffs of the land, when the horses shall have escaped from my control and shall have rushed forth like hurricanes over the earth.'

Forthwith Cuculain sprang out in front of the chariot, and seized them by their mouths and they in their rearing, and with his hands bowed down their heads to the earth, and they knew their master and stood still while they quaked. Laeg collected the birds, and Cuculain secured them to the chariot and to the harness. The birds returned to life and Cuculain cut the binding cords, so that the birds flew over and on either side of the chariot, and singing besides.

In that manner, speeding northward, Cuculain and Laeg drew nigh to Emain Macha. Concobar and the Ultonians happened at that very time to be seeking a druidic response from the prophetess Lavarcam concerning Cuculain and concerning Laeg, for their minds misgave them that beyond the mearings of the Province the lads had come to some hurt, and Lavarcam, answering them, said:

> 'Look to yourselves now ye children of Rury,
> Your destruction and the end of your career are at hand.
> Close all gates, shoot every bar.
> For Dethcaen's nursling, Sualtam's son, draweth nigh.

> 'Verily he is not hurt, but he hath wounded.

Champions the mightiest he hath victoriously overthrown.
Though he come swiftly it is not in flight.
Take good heed now while there is time.
He cometh like night in raiment of darkness,
Starry singing flocks are round his head,
Soon, O Concobar, his unendurable hand will be upon you;
Soon your dead will outnumber your living.'

'Close all the gates of Emain,' cried Concobar, 'and treble-bar all with bars. Look to your weapons ye heroes of the Red Branch. Man the ramparts, and let every bridge be raised.'

So the high king shouted, and his voice rang through the vast and high dun and rolled along the galleries and far-stretching corridors, and was heard by the women of Ulla in their secluded chambers. And at the same time the watchman from the watch-tower cried out. Then the women held council together, and they said:

'Moats and ramparts and strong doors will not repel Cuculain. He will surely o'erleap the moat and burst through the doors and slay many.'

And as they debated together they said that they alone would save the city and defeat the war-demons who had Cuculain in their power. For they said – 'His virginity is with him, and his beautiful shamefastness, and his humility and reverence for women, whether they be old or young, and whether they be comely or not comely. And this was his way always, and now more than formerly since young love hath descended upon him in the form of Emer, daughter of Fargal Manach, King of Lusk in the south.'

Then the women of the Ultonians did a great and memorable deed, and such as was not known to have been done at any time in Erin.

They bade all the men retire into the dun after they had lowered the bridge; and when that was done three tens of them, such as were the most illustrious in rank and famous for accomplishments, and they all in the prime of their youth and beauty, and clad only in the pure raiment of their womanhood, came forth out of the quarters of the women, and in that order, in spite of shame they went to meet him. When Cuculain saw them advancing towards him in lowly wise, with exposed bosom and hands crossed on their breasts, his weapons fell from his hands and the war-demons fled out of him, and low in the chariot he bent down his noble head. By them he was conducted into the dun, into a chamber which they had prepared for him, and they drew water and filled his kieve, and there Laeg ministered to him. He was like one fiery glowing mass – like iron plucked red out of the furnace.

When he had entered his bath the water boiled around him. After he had bathed and when he became calm and cool Laeg put upon him his beautiful banqueting attire, and he came into the great hall lowly and blushing. All were acclaiming and praising him, and he passed up the great hall and made a reverence to the King, and he sat down at the King's footstool. All who saw him marvelled then more at his beauty than at his deeds. He was sick after that, and came very near to death, but in the end he fell into a very deep sleep from which he awoke whole and refreshed, though it was the opinion of many that he would surely die. Cuculain was seventeen years of age when he did these feats.

THE END

BALOR ON TORY ISLAND

Long ago Ri Balor lived on Tory Island, and he lived there because it was prophesied that he was never to die unless he'd be killed by the son of his only daughter.

Balor, to put the daughter in the way that she'd never have a son, went to live on Tory, and built a castle on Tor Mor, a cliff jutting into the ocean. He put twelve women to guard the daughter, and all around the castle he had cords fixed, and every one of them tied to bells, so that no man could come in secret. If any man touched a cord all the bells would ring and give notice, and Balor would seize him.

Balor lived that way, well satisfied. He was full sure that his life was out of danger.

Opposite on the mainland, at Druim na Teine (hill of fire), lived a smith, Gavidin, who had his forge there. The smith owned a cow called Glas Gavlen, and she was his enchanted step-sister.

This cow was called Gavlen because she was giving milk, and she the fifth year without a calf. Glas Gavlen was very choice of food; she would eat no grass but the best. But if the cow ate much good grass there was no measuring the milk she gave; she filled every vessel, and the milk was sweet and rich.

The smith set great value on Glas Gavlen, and no wonder, for she was the first cow that came to Erin, and at that time the only one.

The smith took care of the cow himself, and never let her out of his sight except when working in his forge, and then he had a careful man minding her.

Balor had an eye on Glas Gavlen, and wanted to bring her to Tory for his own use, so he told two agents of his, Maol and Mullag, who were living near Druim na Teine, to get the cow for him. The smith would not part with Glas Gavlen for any price, so there was no way left but to steal her. There was no chance for stealing till one time when three brothers, named Duv, Donn, and Fin, sons of Ceanfaeligh (Kinealy), went to the forge to have three swords made.

'Each man of you is to mind the cow while I am working,' said the smith, 'and if he loses her I'll take the head off him.'

'We will agree to that,' said the brothers.

Duv and Donn went with Glas Gavlen on the first day and the second, and brought her back to the smith safely. When his turn came Fin took the cow out on the third day, but when some distance from the forge he bethought himself and ran back to tell the smith not to make his sword so heavy as those of his brothers. The moment he was inside in the forge Maol and Mullag, Balor's men, stole the cow, and away they went quickly, driving her toward Baile Nass. When they came to the brow of the slope, where the sand begins, they drew her down to the water's edge by the tail, and put her into a boat which they had there prepared and ready.

They sailed toward Tory, but stopped at Inis Bofin (island of the white cow) and put the cow out on land. She drank from a well there, which is called since that time Tobar na Glaise (well of the gray cow). After that they sailed on, and landed the same day at Port na Glaise, on Tory Island.

When Fin came out of the forge he saw nothing of Glas Gavlen, – neither trace nor sign of her. He ran back then with the evil tidings to the smith.

'If you fail to bring her back to me within three days,' said Gavidin, 'I'll take the head off you, according to our bargain. I made the sword to oblige you, and you promised to bring the cow or give your head.'

Away with Fin then, travelling and lamenting, looking for Glas Gavlen. He went toward Baile Nass and came to a place on the strand where a party of men were playing ball. He inquired of them about the cow, but they began to make game of him, he looked so queer in himself, and was so sad. At last one of the players, whose name was

BALOR ON TORY ISLAND

Gial Duv (Black Jaw), came up to Fin and spoke to him: 'Stand aside till the game is over, and I'll talk to you. This is a party of players that you should not interfere with; they are lucht sidhe [people of the mounds, fairies]. I know what your trouble is. I will go with you, and do my best to bring the cow. I know where she is, and if I cannot bring her, no one can.'

They searched down as far as Maheroerty, and went then to Minlara, where a boat was found. They sailed away in the boat, and reached Tory that night a few hours after Maol and Mullag.

'Go now,' said Gial Duv to Fin, 'and ask Balor what would release the cow, and what can you do to earn her. I'll stay here till you come back to me.'

Fin went to Balor and asked the question.

'To get the cow,' said Balor, 'you must eat seven green hides while one inch of a rush-light is burning, and I'll light it myself.'

Fin returned and told Gial Duv. 'Go,' said Gial, 'and tell him you will try to do that. He will put you in a room apart with the hides and take the rush himself. Cut the hides quickly, and if you can cut them I'll make away with them. I'll be there with you, invisible.'

All this was done. Fin cut the hides and Gial Duv put them away. The moment the rush-light was burned Balor came in, and there wasn't a hand's breadth of the hides left.

'I have the seven hides eaten,' said Fin.

'Come to me to-morrow. My daughter will throw the cow's halter. If she throws it to you the cow will be yours.'

Fin was let out of the room then.

'Now,' said Gial Duv, 'I'll take you to Balor's daughter. There is a wall between the castle and the rest of the island, and I'll take you over it. There are cords along the wall everywhere, and whoever tries to pass over will touch them and sound all the bells in the place. I will raise you above them all and take you in without noise. You will go first to Balor's daughter; she will be pleased with you and like you. After that you will see all the other women, and do you be as intimate with them as with Balor's daughter, so that they will not tell that you were in it, and be sure to tell the daughter to throw you the cow's halter tomorrow.'

Fin was taken into the castle by Gial Duv without noise, and he did all that Gial directed. Next day Fin went to Balor and asked for the cow.

'Well, come with me. Let my daughter throw the halter. If she throws it to you the cow will be yours.'

They went. She threw the halter at Fin, and Balor was very angry. 'Oh, daughter,' cried he, 'what have you done?'

'Don't you know,' said she, 'that there is a false cast in every woman's hand? There is a crooked vein in my arm, and I could not help it; that's what gave the halter to Fin.'

Balor had to give the cow and forgive the daughter. Fin took Glas Gavlen to the mainland that day and gave her to the smith.

Before the year was out Gial Duv went to Fin and said, 'Make ready and come with me to Tory; if you don't Balor will find out what happened when you were on the island, and kill his own daughter, with the twelve women and all the children.'

The two went to Tory that evening, and when the children were born the women gave twelve of them to Fin in a blanket, and one, Balor's grandson, by himself in a separate cloth. Fin took his place in the boat with the twelve on his back, and one at his breast. The blanket was fastened at his throat with a dealg (thorn); the thorn broke (there was a great stress on it, for the weather was rough), and the twelve children fell in the water at Sruth Deilg and became seals.

'Oh!' cried Gial, 'the children are lost. Have you Balor's grandson?'

'I have,' answered Fin.

'That is well. We don't care for the others while we have him.'

They brought the child to the mainland, where a nurse was found, but the child was not thriving with her.

'Let us return to Tory with the boy,' said Gial Duv. 'There is nothing that Balor wishes for so much as trees. He has tried often to make trees grow on the island, but it was no use for him. Do you promise that you'll make a grand forest on Tory if he'll let some of the women nurse the child. Tell him that your wife died not long ago. Balor will say, 'How could we find a nurse here when there is no woman on the island who has a child of her own?' You will say that 'tis a power this

BALOR ON TORY ISLAND

child has that whatever woman touches him has her breast full of milk. I will put you in with the women in the evening, and do you tell them what is wanted. The mother is to take the child first when you go in to-morrow, and she will hand him quickly to another and that one to a third, and so on before any can be stopped.'

Fin gave the child to Balor's daughter before her father could come near her; she gave him to one of the women, and he was passed on till all twelve had had him. It was found that all had milk, and Balor consented to let the child be nursed.

Gial Duv made a large fine forest of various trees. For two years Balor was delighted; he was the gladdest man, for all he wanted was trees and shelter on Tory Island.

The child was in good hands now with his mother and the twelve women, and when able to walk, Fin used to bring him out in the daytime. Once he kept him and went to the mainland. The next day a terrible wind rose, and it didn't leave a tree standing on Tory. Balor knew now that the forest was all enchantment and deceit, and said that he would destroy Fin and all his clan for playing such a trick on him. Balor sent his agents and servants to watch Fin and kill him.

Fin was warned by Gial Duv, and took care of himself for a long time, but at last they caught him. It was his custom to hunt in Glen Ath, for there were many deer and much game there in those days, and Fin was very fond of hunting; but he shunned all their ambushes, till one evening when they were lying in wait for him in the bushes by a path which he was travelling for the first time. They leaped up when he was near, caught him, and bound him.

'Take the head off me at one blow,' said he, 'and be done with it.'

They put his head on a stone and cut it off with one blow. In this way died Fin MacKinealy, the father of Balor's grandson. This grandson was a strong youth now. He was a young man, in fact, and his name was Lui Lavada (Lui Longhand). He was called Lavada because his arms were so long that he could tie his shoes without stooping. Lui did not know that he was Balor's grandson. He knew that his father had been killed by Balor's men, and he was waiting to avenge him.

A couple of years later there was a wedding on the mainland, and it was the custom that no one was to begin to eat at a wedding till Maol and Mullag should carve the first slices. They did not come this time in season, and all the guests were impatient.

'I'll carve the meat for you,' said Balor's grandson. With that he carved some slices, and all present began to eat and drink.

After a while Maol and Mullag came, and they were in a great rage because the people were eating, drinking, and enjoying the wedding feast without themselves.

When all had finished eating and drinking, and were ready to go home, Maol said, 'The bride will go with me.'

The bride began to cry when she heard that, and was in great distress. Lui Lavada asked what trouble was on her, and the people told him, that since Balor's two deputies were ruling on the mainland it was their custom at weddings that Maol, the first in authority, should keep company with the bride the first evening, and Mullag the second evening.

'It's time to put a stop to that,' said Lui Lavada, Balor's grandson. With that he walked up to the two and said, 'Ye'll go home out of this as ye are.'

Maol answered with insult, and made an offer to strike him. Lui caught Maol then and split his tongue; he cut a hole in each of his cheeks, and putting one half of the tongue through the left cheek, and the other through the right, he thrust a sliver of wood through the tips of each half. He took Mullag then and treated him in like manner.

The people led the two down to the seashore after that. Lui put Maol in one boat and Mullag in another, and let them go with the wind, which carried them out in the ocean, and there is no account that any man saved them.

Balor swore vengeance on the people for destroying his men, and especially on Lui Lavada. He had an eye in the middle of his forehead which he kept covered always with nine shields of thick leather, so that he might not open his eye and turn it on anything, for no matter what Balor looked at with the naked eye he burned it to ashes. He set out in a rage then from Tory, and never stopped till he landed at Baile Nass and went toward Gavidin's forge. The grandson was there before him, and had a spear ready and red hot.

BALOR ON TORY ISLAND

When Balor had eight shields raised from the evil eye, and was just raising the ninth, Lui Lavada sent the red spear into it. Balor pursued his grandson, who retreated before him, going south, and never stopped till he reached Dun Lui, near Errigal Mountain. There he sat on a rock, wearied and exhausted. While he was sitting there, everything came to his mind that he did since the time that his men stole Glas Gavlen from Gavidin Gow. 'I see it all now,' said he. 'This is my grandson who has given the mortal blow to me. He is the son of my daughter and Fin MacKinealy. No one else could have given that spear cast but him.' With that Balor called to the grandson and said, 'Come near now. Take the head off me and place it above on your own a few moments. You will know everything in the world, and no one will be able to conquer you.'

Lui took the head off his grandfather, and, instead of putting it on his own head, he put it on a rock. The next moment a drop came out of the head, made a thousand pieces of the rock, and dug a hole in the earth three times deeper than Loch Foyle, – the deepest lake in the world up to that time, – and so long that in that hole are the waters of Gweedore Loch, they have been there from that day to this.

* * * * *

The above tale I wrote down on the mainland, where I found also another version, but inferior to this. On Tory itself I found two versions, both incomplete. Though differing in particulars, the argument is the same in all. Balor is represented as living on Tory to escape the doom which threatens him through a coming grandson; he covets the cow Glas Gavlen, and finally gains her through his agents.

The theft of the cow is the first act in a series which ends with the death of Balor at Gweedore, and brings about the fulfilment of the prophecy. In all the variants of the tale Balor is the same unrepentant, unconquerable character, – the man whom nothing can bend, who tries to avenge his own fate after his death by the destruction of his grandson. The grandson does not know whom he is about to kill. He slays Balor to avenge his father, Fin MacKinealy, according to the vendetta of the time.

BALOR OF THE EVIL EYE AND LUI LAVADA HIS GRANDSON

Long ago there were people in Erin called Firbolgs; and they lived undisturbed many years, till a king called Balor Beiman came from Lochlin with great forces, made war on the Firbolgs, killed their king, and drove themselves out of Erin.

The Firbolgs went to Spain; and there they were looking for means of support, but could find none, unless what they got for work in carrying mortar.

They carried mortar, and lived that way till at long last the Spaniards said, 'These people are too many in number; let us drive them out of the country.' So the Spaniards drove out the Firbolgs, and they came back to Erin. In Erin they attacked Balor and his Lochlin men, but were defeated with loss a second time. When they left Erin again, the Firbolgs went to the lands of Gallowna, and there they lived undisturbed and unharmed.

When the Firbolgs were driven out of Erin the second time, Balor Beiman summoned his chief men, and said to them, 'I will go back to Lochlin now and live there in quiet. I am too old to fight with new enemies. I will leave my sons here with you to rule in place of myself; and do ye obey them, and be as brave under them as ye were under me.'

With that Balor left Erin, sailed away, and never stopped till he reached home in Lochlin.

At that time there was a smith in Erin named Gaivnin Gow, and he had a cow called Glas Gownach. The smith had a magic halter with which he used to tie the cow every night.

Glas Gownach travelled three provinces of Erin every day, and came home in the evening; the halter had power over her, and she went always to the halter in the evening if left to herself.

The cow gave milk to every one on her journey each day, – no matter how large the vessels were that people brought, or how many, she filled them; there was no lack of milk in Erin while that cow was in it. She was sent to give food and comfort to all, and she gave it, but especially to poor people.

Balor Beiman had his eye on the cow, and, when going back to Lochlin from Erin, he watched his chance and stole the halter. Gaivnin Gow saw the theft, but too late to prevent it. Balor escaped with the halter, and made off to Lochlin.

Gaivnin Gow ran quickly to Glas Gownach, caught her by the tail, and held her that way till evening, when he drove her home carefully, and shut her up in the forge behind the bellows, where he milked her.

Gaivnin Gow stopped work in his forge now, and did nothing but mind the cow. He went out in the morning, followed her through every place, and brought her back in the evening. He held her tail all the day, and never let go his hold of her till he had her fastened behind the bellows.

The people got milk as before from Glas Gownach wherever she went through the country; but the smith got no milk till he had the cow enclosed in the forge.

The widow of the king of the Firbolgs took a new husband in the land of Gallowna, and had seven sons there. When the eldest, Geali Dianvir, had grown up, she said to him, 'I will give you ships now, and go you to Erin with warriors and good champions to know can we get satisfaction of those people who hunted us out of our country like hares or foxes.'

The son took the ships, and sailed away with champions and heroes, and never stopped till he sailed into Caola Beag (Killybegs, in Donegal). He landed in that place, left his ships safely fastened, and went forward travelling. He never stopped on his way nor halted till he came to a place called Blan Ri. He halted in that place, for before him were three armies fighting.

BALOR OF THE EVIL EYE AND LUI LAVADA HIS GRANDSON

When they saw the new forces coming, the armies stopped fighting.

'Why are ye fighting here with three armies?' asked Dianvir; 'what is the cause of your struggle?'

The leader of one army said, 'We are brothers; our father died not long since; he was king of three provinces, and I think it my right to be king in his place.'

The leader of the second army, the middle brother, said, 'I have as much right to be king after my father as he has.'

The third brother said, 'I have as much right to be king as either of them.'

Neither of the three was willing to yield his claim, or obey one of the others; but they were all ready to fight while their strength lasted.

'Your trouble can be settled easily,' said Dianvir; 'if ye are willing.'

'Settle it, and do us a service,' said the eldest brother.

'I will; but ye must take my judgment and obey it.'

'We will,' said all the brothers. 'We will accept your decision, and do what you tell us.'

'Listen, then,' said Dianvir: 'you, the eldest, will be king for this year. You, the second, will be king in his place the second year; and you, the youngest brother, will be king the third year. The fourth year, you, the eldest brother, will be king again for a year; and so it will go on, and you and your two brothers will be spending time happily all your lives.'

The three brothers agreed, and were glad. The eldest was king that first year. Dianvir went his way; but he had hardly gone out of their sight when the youngest of the three brothers said, 'That man will make trouble for us yet; my advice is to follow him, and put an end to himself and his men before they can harm us.'

'Oh,' said the eldest, 'sure ye would not kill the man who gave us good counsel and settled our difficulty?'

'No matter what he did,' said the youngest; 'he will give you trouble yet if ye let him go. Follow him, put an end to him, or he will put an end to us.'

They sent men after Dianvir. As Dianvir was a stranger in Erin he had no knowledge of the roads: when a lake was before him he was long going around it; when he came to a deep river he was long finding a ford.

Dianvir's men were cut off, most of them fell, and he himself fell with others. A small number escaped to the ships, took one of them, and sailed to the land of Gallowna. They told the queen the whole story, told how they had been treated with treachery.

'I will have satisfaction for my son,' said the mother. 'I will have it without waiting long.' With that she had ships and boats prepared, and went herself with her other sons, and strong forces, to take vengeance on the brothers. The queen and her forces were six weeks sailing hither and over, driven by strong winds, when one morning a sailor at the topmast cried, 'I see land!'

'Is it more or less of it that you see?' asked the queen.

'I see land, the size of a pig's back,' said the sailor, 'and a black back it is.'

They sailed three days and nights longer, and on the fourth morning they were near shore, and landed in Bantry (White Strand). The queen fixed her house at Ardneevy, and prepared for action; but instead of the three brothers it was the sons of Balor she had against her.

War began, and the Lochlin men were getting the upper hand the first days. At some distance from their camp was a well of venom, and into this well they dipped their swords and spears before going to battle, and the man of the enemy who was barely grazed by a weapon dipped in the well was as badly off as the man whose head was taken from him. There was no chance now for the queen's forces, so she called her sons and said to them, 'We'll be destroyed to the last one unless we find help against this venom. Go to the Old Blind Sage, and ask advice of him.'

The sons went to the sage, and the advice they got was this, –

'There is a well of venom not far from the camp of the Lochlin men. Before going to battle they dip their swords and spears in that water, and the enemy who is touched by those weapons that day is killed as surely as if the head had been swept from him. Ye are to get twenty measures of the milk of Glas Gownach, and pour it into that well in the night-time; the milk will be going down in the well and the poison will be rising and going out till it flows away and is lost altogether. Take, then, a hundred swords and spears to Gaivnin Gow, the smith, to put temper on their points and edges. He will do this if ye follow the cow all day for him and bring her home safely in the evening.'

The queen's sons did what the sage advised. The venom went from the well when the cow's milk was poured into it. From that night out the weapons of the Lochlin men were common swords and spears.

When the queen's sons went with the swords and spears to Gaivnin Gow, he said, 'I cannot work for you. I am minding this cow, Glas Gownach, that travels three provinces of Erin every day; I must go with her wherever she goes, bring her home, and put her behind the bellows in the forge every night. If the cow goes from me I am lost, with my wife and children. We have no means of support but her milk.'

'I am as good a man as you,' said the best of the brothers; 'I will mind the cow, and bring her back in the evening.'

The smith let the cow go with him at last, and went to work at the swords and spears. The young man followed the cow faithfully, all day, brought her back in the evening, left her outside the forge, and went in himself. The smith had the swords and spears tempered.

'Where is the cow Glas Gownach?' asked Gaivnin Gow.

'Outside at the door.'

'Bad luck to you, she is gone from me now, gone forever!'

They went out. Not a trace of Glas Gownach. She had gone to Balor Beiman in Lochlin, for he had the halter.

There was a great battle on the following day, the queen fell and her sons, except two. Balor's sons were all killed, and the Lochlin men driven away.

Balor rose up in anger when the news came to Lochlin. 'I'll have satisfaction for my sons,' said he. 'I will burn all Erin!'

Besides his two eyes Balor had a third one, an evil eye, in the middle of his forehead, with the power to burn everything in the world that it looked upon. Over this eye he kept seven steel shields, and a lock on each one of them.

'I will destroy Erin, and no man can stop me,' said Balor; 'for no man can kill me but the son of my daughter. She has no son, and if she had itself, he could kill me only with the red spear made by Gaivnin Gow, and it cast into my eye the moment I raise the last shield from it, when I am standing on Muin Duv[56] [Black Back] to burn Erin.'

One day the two brothers were talking, and Cian, the youngest son of the queen of the Firbolgs, said to his only living brother, 'We have done great harm to Gaivnin Gow. It is by us that the cow went from him, and we should bring her back.'

'That is more than we can do,' said the second brother, 'unless we get help from Bark an Tra, the druid.'

The two brothers went to Bark an Tra, and Cian told their story.

'The work is a hard one; I don't know can you do it,' said the druid; 'but you can try; I will help you. The cow is with Balor Beiman, in Lochlin. He stole her halter when he went from Erin; and she followed it the day your brother left her outside the forge. No man can bring the cow with him unless he has the halter, and it is hard to get that.

'Balor Beiman can be killed only by the son of his daughter; he has her behind seven locked doors. No living person sees the daughter but himself. He sees her every day, takes food and drink to her. To bring back the cow you must make the acquaintance of Balor's daughter. I will give you a cloak of darkness; put it over you, and make your way to Lochlin. When Balor goes to see his daughter, you go with him. He opens one door, goes in and locks it, opens the second, goes in and locks that, and so on. When he is inside in his daughter's chamber the seven doors are locked behind him.'

Cian put on the cloak of darkness, and no man could see him; he went to Lochlin then, and followed Balor to his daughter's chamber. He waited till the night when she was sleeping, went then to her bedside, and put his hand on her heavily.

She screamed, saying, 'Some one is in the chamber.'

Balor came, very angry and with an evil face, to see who was in it. He searched the chamber through, searched many times, found no one. Failing to find any one, he returned to his own place and went to bed. Cian came again and put a heavier hand on Balor's daughter. She roared out that some one was in the chamber. Balor came, searched, and looked several times, and went away. The third time the young man put a still heavier hand on the maiden, and she screamed louder. Balor searched this time more carefully, found no man, and said, 'Oh, you are a torment; it's dreaming you are. You are hoping for some one to be in the world to destroy me, but that is what never will be. If I hear another scream here I will take the head off you surely.'

No sooner was Balor gone this time, and the seven doors locked, than the young man came again, and put a heavier hand than ever on the maiden. She did not scream then; she was in dread of her father, but said slowly, 'Are you a living man or a ghost?'

'I am so and so,' said Cian, 'the best champion in the world, and I have come here to win you.' He talked on till he pleased her, they agreed then. He spent three days in her company. On the fourth day he followed Balor out of the chamber, and away with him back to Erin. He went to Bark an Tra, the druid.

'Were you in Lochlin with Balor?'

'I was.'

'How did you behave?'

'So and so,' said Cian.

'You must be there again at the right time.'

Cian was back in Lochlin at the right time, unseen in his cloak of darkness, and brought away a child with him to Erin. The child was not thriving for three years, hardly lived, and was puny.

'The child is not doing well,' said Cian to the druid.

'The child will do well yet,' answered Bark an Tra. 'Take him now to Lochlin as far as Balor; the child will not thrive till his grandfather calls him by name.'

Cian went to Balor. 'Well,' said Balor, 'who are you and what journey are you on?'

'I am a poor man looking for service.'

'What child is that you have with you?'

'My own child,' said Cian; 'my wife is dead.'

'What can you do?' asked Balor.

'I am the best gardener in the world.'

'I have a better gardener than you,' said Balor.

'You have not. What can your gardener do?'

'The tree that he plants on Monday morning has the finest ripe apples in the world on Saturday night.'

'That's nothing. The tree that I plant in the morning I'll pluck from it in the evening the finest ripe apples you have ever set eyes on.'

'I do not like to have any child near my castle,' said Balor; 'but I will keep you for a time, even with the child, if your wages are not too great for me.'

'I will work a day and a year for the cow.'

Balor agreed to the terms, and took Cian. Balor spoke no word to the child, good or bad, and the boy was not thriving. One day Cian was bringing to Balor a lot of fine apples from one of his trees; he stumbled on the threshold, and the apples fell to the floor. All the people present ran to gather the apples, the child better than others. He worked so nimbly that he picked up two-thirds of all that had fallen, though a whole crowd was picking as well as himself.

'*Tog leat Lui Lavada* [Take away with you Little Long Hand],' cried Balor.

'Oh, he has the name now,' said Cian.

Cian worked his time out then, and said, 'I will take my pay another day.'

'You may take it when you like,' said Balor.

Cian took his son to Erin; the child grew wonderfully after that, and was soon of full strength.

Cian went to the druid.

'The time is near,' said the druid, 'when Balor will stand on Muin Duv. He'll raise his eye-shields; and if the red spear is not put in his eye when the last shield is raised, all Erin will be burned in one flash. Go now and ask Balor Beiman for your wages; say that you want the cow Glas Gownach, for we want her and must have her. He will refuse, dispute, and quarrel, give bad names. You will say that he must pay you, must give the cow or go to judgment. He will go to judgment rather than give the cow; and do you choose his daughter as judge; she will give the cow to you.'

'I will go to judgment,' said Balor, when Cian insisted on getting the cow. 'What judgment will you have?'

BALOR OF THE EVIL EYE AND LUI LAVADA HIS GRANDSON

'My case is a true one,' said Cian. 'I ask no judge but the one yourself will take. I ask no judge but your own daughter.'

'Let her be the judge,' said Balor.

Cian put on his cloak of darkness, and, going to the daughter, explained his case to her. Next day Balor went in and told her all the story of the cow Glas Gownach.

'I must have nine days to think the matter over,' said Balor's daughter.

She got the time, then she asked three days more. On the thirteenth morning Balor went to her and said, 'The judgment must be made today.'

'Well,' said the daughter, 'go out now and stand before the window, you and the gardener, and to whomever the halter comes from me he'll have the cow.'

When they stood in front of the window, she threw the halter to Cian.

'How could you do that?' cried out Balor.

'Oh, father, they say there is always a crooked cast in a woman's hand. I threw toward you; but it's to the gardener the halter went.'

Balor let the cow go. He was very angry, but could not help himself. 'You have Glas Gownach; but I'll have satisfaction in my own time,' cried he, as Cian went away.

'We have troubled you greatly with our work,' said Cian to Gaivnin Gow; 'but here is the cow for you, and with her the halter. You can stay at home now and rest; you need follow her no longer.'

Cian went that night to the druid, and said, 'I have the cow back in Erin.'

'It is well that you have,' answered the druid. 'In five days from this Balor will be here to burn up Erin. He will stand on Muin Duv at daybreak. He will raise all the shields from his eye; and unless a spear made by Gaivnin Gow is hurled into his eye by his grandson that instant, he will have all Erin in flames. You must bring Gaivnin Gow and the forge with you to Muin Duv, have the spear made, and all things prepared there; and your son must be ready to throw the red spear at the right moment.'

CELTIC WARRIORS AND GIANTS

Gaivnin Gow came. They brought the forge, the spear, and all that was needed, put them behind a rock on the side of Muin Duv. On the fifth morning, at daylight, Balor was on the top of Muin Duv; and the instant the last shield reached his upper eyelid Lui Lavada struck him with the spear, and Balor fell dead.

FIN MACCOOL AND THE DAUGHTER OF THE KING OF THE WHITE NATION

One day Fin MacCool and the Fenians of Erin set out on a hunt from the Castle of Rahonain, and never stopped till they came near Brandon Creek, and started a hornless deer in a field called Parcnagri.

Over hills and through valleys they chased the deer till they came to Aun na Vian (the river of the Fenians). The deer sprang from one side of this river toward the other, but before reaching the bank was taken on a spear by Dyeermud.

When the hunt was over, Fin and the Fenians went back to the place where the deer had been started at Parcnagri, for they always returned to the spot where they roused the first game, and there they feasted.

The feast was nearly ready when Fin saw a boat sailing in toward the harbour of Ard na Conye (Smerwick Harbour), and no one on board but a woman.

"'Tis a wonder to me,' said Fin, 'that one woman should manage a boat under sail on the sea. I have a great wish to know who that woman is.'

"'Tis not long I would be in bringing you tidings,' said Dyeermud.

Fin laughed; for Dyeermud was fond of the women. 'I would not refuse you permission to go, but that I myself will go, and be here before our feast is ready.'

Fin went down from Parcnagri, and stood at the strand of Ard na

Conye. Though great was his speed, the woman was there before him, and her boat anchored safely four miles from shore.

Fin saluted the woman with friendly greeting; and she returned the salute in like manner.

'Will you tell me, kind man, where I am now?' asked the woman.

'In the harbour of Ard na Conye.'

'Thanks to you for that answer,' said the woman. 'Can you tell where is Fin MacCool's dwelling-place?'

'Wherever Fin MacCool's dwelling-place is, I am that man myself.'

'Thanks to you a second time,' said the woman; 'and would you play a game of chess for a sentence?'

'I would,' replied Fin, 'if I had my own board and chessmen.'

'I will give you as good as your own,' said the woman.

'I have never refused, and never asked another to play,' said Fin. 'I will play with you.'

They sat down, and Fin won the first game.

'What is your sentence, Fin MacCool?' asked the woman.

'I put you under bonds of heavy enchantment,' said Fin, 'not to eat twice at the one table, nor to sleep two nights in the one bed, till you bring a white steed with red bridle and saddle to me, and the same to each man of the Fenians of Erin.'

'You are very severe, O Fin,' said the woman. 'I beg you to soften the sentence.'

'No,' answered Fin, 'you must give what is asked; I will not soften the sentence.'

'Look behind,' said the woman.

Fin turned, and saw a white steed for himself, and the like for each man of the Fenians of Erin, all with red bridles and saddles.

'Play a second game, now,' said the woman.

They played, and she won.

'Hasten, kind woman,' said Fin, 'and tell me the sentence.'

'Too soon for you to hear it,' said she.

'The sooner I hear it, the better,' said Fin.

'I put you, O Fin, under bonds of heavy enchantment to be my husband till a shovel puts seven of its fulls of earth on your head.'

FIN MACCOOL AND THE DAUGHTER OF THE KING

'Soften the sentence, good woman,' said Fin; 'for this cannot be.'

'The gad may tighten on my throat if I do,' said the woman; 'for you did not soften your sentence on me.'

'Do you stop here,' said Fin to the woman, 'till I give my men the steeds, tell them how I am, and return. But where are the steeds?'

'If I was bound by sentence to bring you the steeds, I was not bound to keep them.'

Fin went his way to Parcnagri, where the Fenians were waiting, and though dinner was ready, no man tasted it from that day to this.

Fin posted his men on watch at various harbours, left Dyeermud on Beann Dyeermud (Dyeermud's peak), just above the harbour of Ard na Conye, and went to the woman. She took his hand; they sprang together, and came down in the woman's boat, which was four miles from land.

The woman weighed anchor, raised sails, and never stopped ploughing the weighty sea till she came to the White Nation in the Eastern World, where her father was king. She entered the harbour, cast anchor, and landed.

'When you were at home,' said the woman to Fin, 'you were Chief of the Fenians of Erin, and held in great honour; I will not that men in this kingdom belittle you, and I am the king's only daughter. From the place where we are standing to my father's castle there is a narrow and a short path. I'll hasten forward on that. There is another way, a broad and long one; do you choose that. I fear that for you there will not be suitable seat and a place in the castle, unless I am there to prepare it before you.'

Fin went the long way, and the woman took the short path. It was many a day since the woman had seen her own father. For twenty-one years she had travelled the world, learning witchcraft and every enchantment. She hurried, and was soon at the door of the castle. Great was the welcome before her, and loud was the joy of her father. Servants came running, one after another, with food, and one thing better than the other.

'Father,' said she, 'I will taste neither food nor drink till you tell me the one thing to please your mind most.'

'My child,' said the king, 'you have but small chance of coming at that. The one thing on earth to delight my mind most is the head of Fin MacCool of Erin. If there was a poor man of my name, he would not be myself if I had that head.'

'Many a year do I know your desire, my father; and it was not for me to come back after twenty-one years without bringing Fin's head. You have it now, without losing one drop of your blood or a single night's rest. Fin is coming hither over the broad road; and do you put men out over against him with music to meet him, and when he comes between your two storehouses, let the men dash him against one corner and the other, and give every reason worse than another to bring him to death.'

The king obeyed his daughter, and sent out guards and musicians.

Fin, going over the broad road, saw men coming with music, and said to himself, 'Great is my joy, or may be my sorrow, for I fear that my life will be ended in trouble.'

The men received Fin with shouts, and, running up, pushed him from side to side till he was bruised and bleeding; then they brought him into the castle.

Glad was the king, and far was the laugh heard that he let out of himself at sight of Fin MacCool.

The king gave command then to bind the captive, putting seven knots of cord on every joint of his body, to throw him into a deep vault, and give him one ounce of black bread with a pint of cold water each day.

Fin was put in the vault, and a very old little woman brought his daily allowance of food.

On his eighth day in prison, Fin said to the old little woman, 'Go now to the king, and say that I have a petition. I ask not my head, as I would not get it; but say that my right arm is rotting. I ask to be free in the garden for one hour; let him send with me men, if he chooses.'

The old woman told the request; and the king said, 'I will grant that with willingness; for it will not take his head from me.'

Thirty armed men were sent, and Fin was set free in the garden. While walking, he asked the chief of the thirty, 'Have you musical instruments?'

FIN MACCOOL AND THE DAUGHTER OF THE KING

'We have not,' said the chief; 'we forgot them. If they were here, we would give music; for I pity you, Fin MacCool.'

'When I was at home,' said Fin, 'having the care and charge over men, we had music; and, if it please you, I will play some of the music of Erin.'

'I would be more than glad if you would do that,' said the chief.

The Fenians of Erin had a horn called the borabu; and when one of them went wandering he took the borabu with him, as Fin had done this time. It was the only instrument on which he could play. Fin blew the horn, and the sound of it came to Beann Dyeermud from the Eastern World. Dyeermud himself was in deep sleep at the moment; but the sound entered his right ear and came out through the left. The spring that he made then took him across seven ridges of land before he was firm on his feet. Dyeermud, wiping his eyes, said, 'Great is the trouble that is on you, Fin; for the sound of the borabu has never yet entered my right ear unless you were in peril.'

Then, going at a spring to Cuas a Wudig, he found the remains of an old currachan, and, drawing out a chisel, knife, and axe, made a fine boat of the old one. With one kick of his right foot, he sent the boat seven leagues from land, and, following with a bound, dropped into it. He hoisted sails, not knowing whither to go, north, south, east, or west, but held on his way, and ploughed the mighty ocean before him, till, as good luck would have it, he reached the same harbour to which the woman had come with Fin MacCool.

Dyeermud saw the boat which had brought them, and said, laughing heartily, 'I have tidings of Fin; he's in this kingdom in some place, for this is the boat that brought him from Erin.'

Dyeermud cast anchor, and, landing, drew his sword; and a man seeing his look at that moment would have wished to be twenty miles distant. On he went, walking, till he had passed through a broad tract of country. On the high-road, he saw men, women, and children all going one way, and none any other. High and low, they were hurrying and hastening; the man behind outstripping the man in front.

Dyeermud sat on a ditch to rest, and soon a wayfarer halted in front of him. 'Where are these people all hastening?' asked Dyeermud.

'From what country or place are you,' asked the man, 'not to know whither all these people are going?'

'Surely I am not of this place or your country,' said Dyeermud; 'and I care not to know whither you or these people are going, since you cannot give a civil answer to an honest question.'

'Be patient, good man,' said the wayfarer 'From what country or place are you?'

'From Erin,' said Dyeermud.

'I suppose, then, you have known Fin MacCool, or have heard of him?'

'I have, indeed,' said Dyeermud.

'If you take my advice,' said the wayfaring man, 'you'll go out on the same road by which you came in, or else not acknowledge Fin MacCool of Erin, for that man will be hanged this day before the king's castle; the gallows is ready and built for him. When the life is gone out of him, his head will be struck off, and left as a plaything to please the king's mind forever. The body is to be dragged between four wild horses; and the same will be done to you, if you acknowledge Fin MacCool of Erin.'

'I thank you for your answer,' said Dyeermud; 'and only because I don't like to lay a weighty hand on you, you would never again give advice like that to a man of the Fenians of Erin. But show me the way to the castle.'

'If you were on the top of that mountain,' said the wayfarer, pointing northward, 'you would see the king's castle.'

Dyeermud went on in strong haste, and from the mountain-top saw the king's castle. On the green field in front of it so many people had gathered to see Fin MacCool's death, that if a pin were to drop from the middle of the sky it could not fall without striking the head of man, woman, or child. When Dyeermud came down to the field, it was useless to ask for room or for passage, since each wished himself to be nearest the place of Fin's death. Dyeermud drew his sword; and as a mower goes through the grass of a meadow on a harvest day, or a hawk through a flock of starlings on a chilly March morning, so did Dyeermud cut his way through the crowd till he came to the gallows. He turned then toward the castle, struck the pole of combat, and far was

FIN MACCOOL AND THE DAUGHTER OF THE KING

the sound of his blow heard. The king put his head through the window.

'Who struck that blow?' asked the king. 'He must be an enemy!'

'You could not expect a friend to do the like of that,' replied Dyeermud. 'I struck the blow.'

'Who are you?' cried the king.

'My name when in Erin is Dyeermud.'

'What brought you hither?' asked the king.

'I came,' replied Dyeermud, 'to succour my chief, Fin MacCool.'

The king let a laugh out of him, and asked, 'Have any more men come besides you?'

'When you finish with me, you may be looking for others,' said Dyeermud.

'What do you want to-day?' asked the king.

'I want to see Fin MacCool, or to fight for him.'

'Fight you may,' said the king; 'but see him you will not.'

'Well,' said Dyeermud, 'it is too early in the evening for me to rest without having the blood of enemies on my sword, so send out against me seven hundred of your best-armed men on my right hand, seven hundred on my left, seven hundred behind me, and twenty one hundred before my eyesight.'

Fin's death was delayed; and the men that he asked for put out against Dyeermud. Coming sunset, he had the last head cut from the last body, and, going through his day's work, made heaps of the bodies, and piles of the heads.

'Will you give me shelter from the night air?' asked Dyeermud, then turning to the castle.

'I will, and welcome,' said the king, pointing to a long house at a distance.

Dyeermud went to the long house, and to his wonder saw there a troop of wild small men without faith, but no food, fire, or bed. These men were the agents of the king, who put to death all people who went against his law. Though a small race of people, they were strong through their numbers.

When Dyeermud entered, they rose, and began to fill every cranny and crack they could find in the building.

'Why are you doing that?' inquired Dyeermud.

'For fear that you might escape; for it's our duty to eat you.'

Dyeermud then seized by the ankles the one who gave him this answer, and flailed the others with this man, till he wore him down to the two shin-bones; all the others were killed saving one, who was chief. The small chief untouched by Dyeermud fell on his knees, and cried out, 'Spare my head! O Dyeermud, there is not a place where you will put one foot, in which I will not put my two feet, nor a place on which you'll put one hand, in which I will not put my two hands; and I can be a good servant to you.'

'No man ever asked his head of me with peace, but I gave it to him,' said Dyeermud.

Sitting down then, Dyeermud asked, 'Have you any food?'

'I have not,' said the small chief. 'We have nothing to eat but men sent here from one time to another. If you go to the king's bakery, you may find loaves of bread.'

Dyeermud went to the baker, and asked, 'Will you give me two loaves of bread?'

'Hardened ruffian,' said the baker, 'how dare you come to this place for bread, or any other thing, you who killed so many of our friends and near neighbours? Go out of this, or I'll burn you in the oven.'

'I am thankful,' said Dyeermud; 'but before you can do to me what you threaten, I will do the same to you.'

With that he opened the oven-door, threw in the baker, and burned him to death. Then he caught up as much bread as he could carry, and went to the Long house; but, being used to good food, could not eat bread alone, and asked the small chief, 'Where can I find drink and meat to go with the bread?'

'There is a slaughter-house behind us, not far from here,' said the chief, 'and the head butcher might give you a piece to roast or boil.'

Dyeermud went then to the butcher. 'Will you give me meat for supper?' asked he.

'You scoundrel from Erin, if you don't leave this place I'll cut off your head on the block here, and separate it from the body.'

'Never have I met better people to oblige a stranger; but before you

FIN MACCOOL AND THE DAUGHTER OF THE KING

can do to me what you promise, I will do the like to you.'

So Dyeermud caught the butcher, stretched him across the block, and with the butcher's own cleaver struck the head off him.

Turning around, Dyeermud saw two fine stalled bullocks dressed for the king's table. Taking one under each arm, he brought them to the long house, and cut them up with his sword; then the small chief cooked nicely what was needed. The two ate a hearty supper.

Next morning Dyeermud rose up refreshed, and went to the castle, where he struck the pole of combat.

'What is your wish?' asked the king.

'To see Fin MacCool, or get battle.'

'How many men do you wish for?'

'One thousand of your best armed men on my right hand, as many on my left, as many behind me, and twice three thousand in front of my eyesight.'

The champions were sent out to Dyeermud. They went at him, and he at them; they were that way all day, and when the sun was setting there was not a man of the nine thousand that had his head on him.

In the evening he made piles of the bodies and heaps of the heads.

Then he went back to the long house, and it was better there than the first night; the small chief had food and drink ready in plenty.

The combats continued for seven days in succession as on this day. On the eighth morning, when Dyeermud appeared, the king asked for a truce.

'I will grant it,' said Dyeermud, 'if you give me a sight of Fin MacCool.'

'A sight of Fin MacCool you are not to have,' said the king, 'till you bring the hound-whelp with the golden chain.'

'Where can I find that Whelp?' inquired Dyeermud.

'The world is wide,' said the king. 'Follow your nose. It will lead you. If I were to say 'tis in the west the whelp is, maybe 'tis in the east he'd be; or in the north, maybe he'd be in the south. So here and now you cannot blame me if I say not where he is.'

'Well,' said Dyeermud, 'as I am going for the whelp, I ask you to loose Fin MacCool from what bonds he is in, to place him in the best chamber of your castle, to give him the best food and drink, the best bed to lie on, and, besides, the amusements most pleasing to his mind.'

'What you ask shall be granted,' said the king, who thought to himself, 'Your head and Fin's will be mine in the end.'

Dyeermud went home to the long house, sat down in his chair, and gloomy was his face.

'O Dyeermud,' said the small chief, 'you are not coming in with such looks, nor so bright in the face, as when you left here this morning. I'll lay my head as a wager that you are sent to bring the hound-whelp with the golden chain.'

'True,' said Dyeermud, 'and where to find him I know not.'

'Eat your supper, then sleep, and to-morrow I'll show you where that whelp is. Indeed, it is the task you have on you; for many a good champion lost his head in striving to come at that whelp.'

Next morning Dyeermud and the small chief set out, and toward evening they came within sight of a grand, splendid castle.

'Now,' said the small chief, 'this castle was built by the Red Gruagach Blind-on-One-Side; within is the hound-whelp with the golden chain; and now let me see what you'll do.'

Dyeermud entered the castle, where he found a great chamber, and in it the gruagach asleep. The hound was tied to the gruagach's bed with a golden chain. Untying the chain from the bed, Dyeermud carried whelp and chain with him under his arm, and hurried on homeward. When he had gone three miles of road, he turned to the small chief and said, 'That was a mean act I did to the gruagach.'

'What's on you now?' asked the small chief.

'It would be hard for a man to call me anything higher than a thief; for I have only stolen the man's whelp and golden chain.' So Dyeermud went back to the gruagach, and put the hound-whelp and chain where he had found them. As the gruagach was sleeping, Dyeermud struck a slight blow on his face to rouse him.

'Oh,' said the gruagach, 'I catch the foul smell of a man from Erin. He must be Dyeermud, who has destroyed the champions of our country.'

'I am the man that you mention,' said Dyeermud; 'and I am not here

FIN MACCOOL AND THE DAUGHTER OF THE KING

to ask satisfaction of you or thanks, but to wear out my anger on your body and flesh, if you refuse what I want of you.'

'And what is it that you want of me?' asked the gruagach.

'The hound-whelp with the golden chain.'

'You will not get him from me, nor will another.'

'Be on your feet, then,' said Dyeermud. 'The whelp is mine, or your head in place of him; if not, you'll have my head.'

One champion put his back to the front wall, and the other to the rear wall; then the two went at each other wrestling, and were that way till the roof of the house was ready to fly from the walls, such was the strength in the hands of the combatants.

'Shame on you both!' cried the gruagach's wife, running out. 'Shame on two men like you to be tumbling the house on my children.'

'True,' said Dyeermud. And the two, without letting go the hold that they had, went through the roof with one bound, and came down on the field outside. The first wheel that Dyeermud knocked out of the gruagach, he put him in the hard ground to his ankles, the second to his hips, and the third to his neck.

'Suffer your head to be cut off, O gruagach.'

'Spare me, Dyeermud, and you'll get the hound-whelp with the golden chain, and my good wish and desire.'

'If you had said that at first, you would not have gone through this hardship or kindled my anger,' said Dyeermud. With that he pulled out the gruagach, and spared his head.

The two spent that night as two brothers, eating and drinking of the best, and in the morning the gruagach gave Dyeermud the whelp with the golden chain.

Dyeermud went home with the small chief, and went to the castle next morning.

'Have you brought the hound-whelp with the golden chain?' asked the king.

'I have,' answered Dyeermud; 'and I had no trouble in bringing them. Here they are before you.'

'Well, am I to have them now?' asked the king.

'You are not,' answered Dyeermud. 'If I was bound to bring them, I was not bound to give them to you. The man who reared this whelp has a better right to him than you or I.'

Then Dyeermud went home to the long house, followed by the small chief; and the next morning he asked battle of the king.

'I am not ready for battle to-day,' said the king.

'Am I to get sight of Fin MacCool?' inquired Dyeermud.

'You are not,' said the king, 'till you bring me an account of how the Rueful Knight Without-Laughter lost his eye and his laugh.'

'Where can I find that knight?' asked Dyeermud.

'The world is wide,' said the king; 'and it is for you alone to make out where that man is.'

Dyeermud went home to the long house, sat in his chair, dropped his head, and was gloomy.

'O Dyeermud,' said the small chief, 'something has gone wrong to-day, and I'll lay my head that you are sent to get knowledge of the Rueful Knight Without-Laughter; but sit down and take supper, then sleep, and to-morrow you'll not go astray; I'll lead you to where that man lives.'

Next morning the two set out together, that evening reached the gruagach's castle, where there was many a welcome before them, and not like the first time. The whelp was returned to his owner; and that night was spent in pleasure by the gruagach, Dyeermud, and the small chief.

The next morning Dyeermud went forward attended by his two friends, and toward evening came in sight of a large splendid castle. Dyeermud approached it, and when he went in, saw that he had never before set foot in a grander building.

The Rueful Knight Without-Laughter was sitting alone in his parlor at a great heavy table. His face, resting on the palm of one hand, was worn by it; his elbow, placed on the table, had worn a deep trench in the table; and there he sat, trusting to the one eye that was left him.

Dyeermud shook the sleeping man gently; and when he woke, the knight welcomed Dyeermud as one of the Fenians of Erin. Dinner was made ready for all; and when they sat down at the table, Dyeermud thrust his fork in the meat as a sign of request. 'Is there something you wish to know?' asked the knight.

FIN MACCOOL AND THE DAUGHTER OF THE KING

'There is,' answered Dyeermud.

'All in my power or possession is for you, except one thing,' said the knight, 'and ask not for that.'

'It is that thing that brought me,' said Dyeermud. 'I'll take no refusal. I'll have your head or that knowledge.'

'Well, Dyeermud, eat your dinner, and then I will tell you; though I have never told any one yet, not even my own lawful wife.'

When the dinner was over, the knight told his story to Dyeermud, as follows, –

'I was living once in this place here, both happy and well. I had twelve sons of my own and my own wife. Each of my twelve sons had his pack of hounds. I and my wife had one pack between us. On a May morning after breakfast, I and my sons set out to hunt. We started a deer without horns, and, rushing forward in chase of her, followed on swiftly all day. Toward evening the deer disappeared in a cave. In we raced after her, and found ourselves soon in the land of small men, but saw not a trace of the deer.

'Going to a great lofty castle, we entered, and found many people inside. The king of the small men bade us welcome, and asked had I men to prepare us a dinner. I said that I had my own twelve sons. The small men then brought in from a forest twelve wild boars. I put down twelve kettles with water to scald and dress the game. When the water was boiling, it was of no use to us; and we could not have softened with it one bristle on the wild boars from that day to this. Then a small man, putting the twelve boars in a row with the head of one near the tail of the other, took from the hall-door a whistle, and, blowing first on one side of the row and then on the other, made all the twelve white and clean; then he dressed, cut, and cooked them, and we all ate to our own satisfaction.

'In the course of the evening, the king of the small men asked had I anyone who could shorten the night by showing action. I said that I had my own twelve sons. Twelve small men now rose, and drew out a long weighty chain, holding one end in their hands. My sons caught the other end, pulled against the twelve small men, and the small men against them; but the small men soon threw a loop of the chain around the necks of my twelve sons, and swept the heads off them; one of the small men came then with a long knife, and, opening the breasts of my sons, took out their twelve hearts, and put them all on a dish; then they pushed me to a bench, and I had to sit with my twelve sons stretched dead there before me. Now they brought the dish to make me eat the twelve hearts for my supper. When I would not, they drove them down my throat, and gave me a blow of a fist that knocked one eye out of me. They left me that way in torment till morning; then they opened the door, and threw me out of the castle.

'From that day to this I have not seen my children, nor a trace of them; and 'tis just twenty-one years, coming May-day, since I lost my twelve sons and my eye. There is not a May-day but the deer comes to this castle and shouts, "Here is the deer; but where are the hunters to follow?" Now you have the knowledge, Dyeermud, of how I lost my eye and my laugh.'

'Well,' asked Dyeermud, 'will May-day come soon in this country?'

'To-morrow, as early as you will rise.'

'Is there any chance that the deer will come in the morning?'

'There is,' said the knight; 'and you'll not have much of the morning behind you when she'll give a call.'

Next morning the deer shouted, 'Here is the deer; but where are the hunters to follow?' and made away swiftly.

Dyeermud, the small chief, the gruagach, and the knight hurried on in pursuit. Coming evening, the knight saw the cave, and called out to Dyeermud, 'Have a care of that place; for 'tis there she will enter.'

When the deer reached the cave, Dyeermud gave a kick with his right foot, and struck off one half her hind-quarter.

Barely was this done, when out rushed a dreadful and ugly old hag, with every tooth in her upper jaw a yard long, and she screaming, 'You hungry, scorched scoundrel from Erin, how dared you ruin the sport of the small men?'

The words were hardly out of her mouth, when Dyeermud made at her with his fist, and sent jaws and teeth down her throat. What the old hag did not swallow, went half a mile into the country behind her.

FIN MACCOOL AND THE DAUGHTER OF THE KING

The hag raced on through the land of the small men, and Dyeermud with his forces made after her. When they came to the castle, the king let a loud laugh out of him.

'Why do you give such a laugh?' inquired Dyeermud.

'I thought that the knight had enough the first time he came to this castle.'

'This proves to you that he had not,' said Dyeermud; 'or he would not be in it the second time.'

'Well,' asked the king of the knight, 'have you any man now to cook dinner?'

'He has,' said Dyeermud; 'and it's long since you or he had the like of him. I'll cook your dinner, and we'll find the food.'

Out they went to a forest, and brought in twelve wild boars. Dyeermud skinned the game with his sword, dressed, cut, and cooked it. All ate to satisfaction.

Later on in the evening, the king asked the knight, 'Have you any man to show action?'

'He has,' said Dyeermud, 'if you will put out the same twelve men as you did the first evening.'

The king put them out; and Dyeermud took the end of the chain to pull against them. He pulled till he sank in the floor to his ankles; then he made a whirl of the chain, and swept their twelve heads off the small men. He opened the twelve, put their hearts on a plate, and made the king eat them. 'You forced the knight to swallow the hearts of his own sons,' said Dyeermud.

'Walk out of the castle, and punish us no more,' cried the king. 'I'll let out to the knight his sons, with their horses and hounds, and his own horse and hounds, if you will not come to this kingdom again.'

'We will go if you do that,' said Dyeermud; 'but you are not to offend the knight or his people; if you do, I am a better guide to find you a second time than I was the first.'

The king took his rod of enchantment, went out to twelve stones, struck the first, out came the first son on horseback, and a pack of hounds after him. The king struck stone after stone till he put the twelve sons in front of the castle, with their horses and hounds; then he struck the thirteenth stone, and the horse and hounds of the knight appeared.

The knight looked around, and saw his eye in the hole of the chimney, and as much soot on it as would manure land under two stone of seed-potatoes.

'Look at my eye,' said the knight.

Dyeermud looked. Then the king put the eye in the head of the knight, who could see with it better than when he had it before.

Out they went now from the king, safe and sound, and never stopped till they reached the knight's castle for dinner. When dinner was over, Dyeermud, the gruagach, and the small chief hastened on to the gruagach's castle, and slept there.

Next day Dyeermud and the small chief went home. On the following morning, Dyeermud went to the king, told him the Rueful Knight's story, and said, 'Now I must have battle, or a sight of Fin MacCool.'

'Battle I'll not give you,' said the king; 'and a sight of Fin MacCool you'll not have till you tell me what happened to the Lad of True Tales.'

'I am sorry,' said Dyeermud, 'that this was not said by you sooner. It is late for me now to be tearing my shoes on strange roads, and tiring my feet in a foreign land.' With that he sprang at the king, brought him down by the throat from the window to the ground, and there broke every bone in his body. Then he put the castle foundation upward, looking for Fin, and destroying all that he met, but could not find Fin till he met the old little woman.

'O Dyeermud,' said she, 'spare my head. I am more than a hundred years old. I have been faithful to Fin since he came here. I have never refused to do what he asked of me.'

'Your head shall be spared,' replied Dyeermud, 'though old life is as dear to you as it is to young people; and take me now to where Fin is.'

Dyeermud went with the old little woman to the door of Fin's chamber, and knocked. Fin knew the knock, and cried out, 'Reach me your sword.'

'Take it,' said Dyeermud.

Fin's strength was trebled at sight of Dyeermud; and when he

FIN MACCOOL AND THE DAUGHTER OF THE KING

grasped the sword, he swore by it, saying, 'I will cut off your head if you come a foot nearer.'

'You are not in your mind to speak thus to the man who has gone through so much for you.'

'I am in my mind,' said Fin; 'but if we were to close our arms embracing each other in friendship, we could not open them for seven days and nights. Now, the woman who brought me from Ard na Conye, the bay which we love most in Erin, save Fintra, will be here soon. Though there was nothing on earth to please the King of the White Nation more than my head, there is another good man in the world, and the king wishes his head as greatly as mine. The daughter has gone, and is using her highest endeavour to bring that head to her father; so hasten on to the boat, Dyeermud, I will follow. If you find food, take it with you.'

Dyeermud hurried off. In passing through the king's meadow he saw two fat bullocks grazing. He caught them, and, clapping one under each arm, ran off to the boat. When Fin came, he found both bullocks skinned and dressed there before him.

They weighed anchor now and raised sails for Erin, ploughing the weighty sea before them night and day. Once Fin said to Dyeermud, 'Look behind.' Dyeermud looked, but saw nothing.

Three hours later, Fin said, 'Look behind, and look keenly.'

Dyeermud looked, and cried, 'I see behind us in the sky some bird like an eagle, and flashes of fire blazing out from her beak.'

'Oh, we are caught at last, and it's a bad place we are in on the sea; we cannot fight here.'

The bird was coming nearer, and gaining; but the wind favored, filled every sail, and sent them bounding along till they were within five leagues of land; then they made one spring, and came down in Ferriter's Cove.

No sooner had they landed, than the bird perched on the boat, turned it over, stood on the bottom, and from that saw Fin and Dyeermud on land. She made for them; and the moment she touched shore became a woman.

She rushed to Fin, caught him in her arms most lovingly, and said, turning to Dyeermud, 'You are the wicked man who put words between me and my husband and parted us.'

Then, turning to Fin, she said, 'Now, my darling, come home with me. You will be King of the White Nation, and I, your loving wife.'

'Right and true for you,' said Dyeermud. 'It's the good wife and friend you were to this man; and now I ask how long must he be your husband?'

'Till a shovel puts seven of its fulls of earth on his head.'

Dyeermud drew his sword, and struck a champion's blow on a ridge of land that was near him; he was so enraged that he made a deep glen with that blow; then he caught Fin, and, stretching him in the glen, thrust his sword in the earth, and, throwing it as with a shovel on Fin, counted one, two, three, four, five, six, seven. 'Your time is up with Fin,' said he to the king's daughter; 'he is in his own country, and you are a stranger. Take him a second time if you can, and I pledge you the faith of a champion that I will not put words between you.'

The woman stooped down to put away the seven shovels of earth, and said to Fin while she was working, 'We'll both be happy this time.'

With that Dyeermud gave her one blow of his fist on the left ear, and sent her spinning through the air. She never stopped till she fell at the edge of the ocean, and became Fail Mahisht; and not another cliff in Erin has so many limpets and periwinkles on it as that one.

So the daughter of the King of the White Nation gives much food to people in Erin from that day to this.

FIN MACCOOL, THE THREE GIANTS, AND THE SMALL MEN

On a day of the days when Fin MacCool was living at Rahin, he went out to walk near Fintra. He had many cows and sheep at that time, and was going among his cattle, when all at once he saw a big man coming in from the sea.

At first he saw the man's head and shoulders, then half his body, and at last his whole body. When the big man stood on the strand, he saluted Fin. Fin returned the salute, and asked, 'Who are you, and what brought you to Erin?'

'I have come from the King of the Big Men; and I want to see Fin MacCool.'

'Fin MacCool is not at home now,' said Fin. 'Are you here with a message?'

'I am,' said the big man.

'I will give the message to Fin MacCool when he comes home; there is no one he trusts more than me.'

'My master, the King of the Big Men, has heard much of Fin MacCool, and invites him to come to his castle. The king lost two children. Some one came in the night and stole them. Though guarded with wonderful strictness, the children were carried away. The king fears to lose a third child soon, unless Fin MacCool comes to advise and assist him.'

'I will give that message to Fin MacCool,' said Fin.

The big man left good health with Fin, then turned and went forward, going deeper till his head disappeared under water.

A few days later Fin was walking in the same place where he had met the messenger from the King of the Big Men, and he saw some very small men playing hurley on the strand. He went to them, and spoke. They answered, and called him King of the Fenians.

'You seem to know me,' said Fin.

'We do indeed, and we know you very well,' said the small men.

'Who are you?' asked Fin, 'or what can you do?'

'Oh, we have many virtues,' replied they.

'What virtue have you?' asked Fin, turning to the biggest of the small men.

'Well, whenever I sit down in any place I stay in it as long as I like; no man can lift me; no power can take me out of it.'

'What is your name?' asked Fin.

'Lazy Back,' said the little fellow. 'No man can stir me when I sit down.'

'How am I to know that you have that virtue?' asked Fin.

'You are a strong man yourself,' answered Lazy Back; 'give me a trial.'

The little man sat down. Fin caught him with one hand, and tried to raise him; but not a stir could he take out of Lazy Back.

'Try with both hands now,' said Lazy Back.

Fin tried with both hands, tried with all the strength that was in him, but could not move the little man.

'What is your virtue?' asked Fin, turning to the second man; 'and who are you?'

'My name is Hearing Ear.'

'What can you hear?'

'I can hear a whisper in the Eastern World, and I sitting in this place.'

'What is your name?' asked Fin of the third player.

'My name is Far Feeler.'

'What can you feel?' asked Fin.

'I can feel an ivy-leaf falling at the Eastern World, and I playing here at Fintra.'

'What is your name?' asked Fin, turning to the fourth player.

'My name is Knowing Man.'

FIN MACCOOL, THE THREE GIANTS, AND THE SMALL MEN

'What do you know?'

'I know all that will happen in every part of the world.'

'What power have you, and who are you?' asked Fin of the fifth man.

'I am called Always Taking; I steal.'

'What can you steal?'

'Whatever I set my mind on. I can steal the eggs from a snipe, and she sitting on them; and the snipe is the wariest bird in existence.'

'What can you do?' asked Fin, looking at the sixth man.

'My name is Climber. I can climb the highest castle in the world, though its sides were as slippery as glass.'

'Who are you?' asked he of the seventh stranger.

'I am called Bowman.'

'What can you do?'

'I can hit any midge out of a cloud of midges dancing in the air.'

'You have good eyesight,' said Fin, 'and good aim as well.

'Who are you?' asked Fin of the eighth.

'I am called Three Sticks. I understand woodwork.'

'What can you do?' asked Fin.

'I can make anything I please out of wood.'

'Can you make a ship?'

'I can.'

'How long would it take you to make one?'

'While you would be turning on your heel.'

He took a chip of wood then from the shore, and asked Fin to turn on his heel. While Fin was turning, Three Sticks flung the piece of wood out on the sea, and there it became a beautiful ship.

'Well, have you the ship made?' asked Fin, looking on the strand.

'There it is,' said Three Sticks, 'floating outside.'

Fin looked, and saw the finest vessel that ever sailed on the deep sea; the butt of no feather was in, nor the tip of one out, except one brown-backed red feather that stood at the top of the mast, and that making music and sport to encourage whatever champion would come on board.

'Will you all take service with me?' asked Fin, looking at the eight small strangers. 'I wish to go to the kingdom of the Big Men. Will you guide me on the journey, and help me?'

'We are willing to serve you,' answered they. 'There is no part of the world to which we cannot guide you.'

'What are your wages?' asked Fin.

'Five gold-pieces to each man of us for a day and a year.'

'How much time do we need for the journey to the kingdom of the Big Men?'

'Not many days,' said Knowing Man.

Stores and provisions were put on the ship. Fin and the small men went on board, and set sail; before many days they arrived at the kingdom of the Big Men, and drew up their ship high and dry. They set out then for the castle of the king; and no greater wonder was ever seen in that place than Fin and his eight little men.

The king invited Fin and his company to a great feast. At the end of the feast, the king said, 'My third son was born to-day. My first son was taken away on the night after his birth, and so was my second. I am full sure that this one will be taken from me to-night.'

'I will guard the child,' said Fin; 'and if I let your son go with any one, I will give you my head.'

The king was satisfied. Fin asked for a strong chamber and two nurses. The strongest chamber in the castle was made ready; then Fin and his men, with the child and two nurses, took their places inside.

'Do you know what will happen to-night?' asked Knowing Man.

'I do not,' replied Fin; 'and I do not like to chew my thumb.[57] You can tell me.'

'You gave your head in pledge,' said Knowing Man, 'for the safety of the child; and you were a strange man to do so, for the child will be taken from this to-night.'

'Do you say that?' asked Fin.

'I do. And do you know who will do it?'

'I do not.'

'I will tell you. In the Eastern World lives a sister of this king, a savage hag and a terrible witch. This hag went to the Eastern World

FIN MACCOOL, THE THREE GIANTS, AND THE SMALL MEN

because she had a dispute with her brother. She is ungrateful, and full of malice; she comes now and steals away her brother's children to leave him without heirs to his kingdom. When she finds this room closed on every side, and sees no other way of reaching the child, she will climb to the roof, and stretch her arm down to catch the king's little son, and take him away with her.'

Lazy Back sat down near the hearth, and swore a great oath that if the hag thrust her hand down, he would hold her or keep the hand.

A little after midnight, Hearing Ear said, 'I hear the hag; she is making ready to leave her castle in the Eastern World, and giving strict orders to guard the two children while she is gone.'

'Well,' said Far Feeler, 'now I feel her going up through her own castle; now I feel her going out through the door on the roof. Her castle has no entrance except an opening in the roof, and the walls of it are as slippery as glass.'

'You will warn me when she is coming,' said Fin to Hearing Ear.

'Oh, I will,' said Hearing Ear; 'I will not forget that.'

In a little while the hag was at the castle, and going around it trying to enter. Although the castle was surrounded by sentries, not one of them saw her; for she was invisible, through power of enchantment.

'She has come,' said Hearing Ear; 'she is walking around the castle. Now is the time to watch her well.'

A few moments later, she thrust her arm down the chimney; and no sooner was it down than Lazy Back caught her hand. When she felt her hand caught, she struggled greatly; but Lazy Back kept the hold that he had, and nothing could stir him. At last the arm left the shoulder of the hag. Lazy Back drew the arm down the chimney. All looked at it with amazement; and while the nurses were wondering at the arm, and Fin measuring its length and its thickness, they forgot the child. The hag thrust her other arm down then, caught the child, and hurried away home with it. When the nurses saw that the child was gone, they screamed; and Fin said, –

'It would be better for us to hurry to our vessel, and leave the country before the king is up in the morning; he will destroy us all for losing his son.'

'We will not do that,' said the little men. 'Late as it is, we will follow the hag, and bring back the child.'

They set out that moment; and since Fin could not keep up with the little men, Lazy Back took him on his shoulder: and, in the twinkle of an eye, they reached the ship, and set sail for the Eastern World.

Indeed, they were not long on the journey; for they were enchanted. When they came to land near the hag's castle, Fin, Bowman, and two others remained on the vessel. Climber, Thief, and the rest went for the child.

'Where are you, Climber?' asked Thief, when they were at the wall.

'Here,' said Climber.

'Take me to the top of the castle.'

Climber took Thief on his back, and climbed like a butterfly to the top of the building; then Thief crept down into the castle, and returned quickly with the youngest of the children.

'Take this one down to our comrades, and hurry back to me.'

Climber went down, and hastened up again. Thief had another of the children at the top of the castle before him. Climber took that down, with orders from Thief to carry the two children to the vessel. Then he returned a third time, and Thief had the third child.

'Take this one, and come for me,' said Thief.

The little men at the foot of the castle ran off to the ship with the last child. Nimble as Thief was, he could not have taken the children at another time. All the servants were busied with the hag, who was suffering terribly from the loss of her arm. They forgot the children for a short time.

Climber took Thief to the ground, and they started at full speed toward the ship. When they came, Fin set sail for the kingdom of the Big Men.

'We shall be pursued right away,' said Knowing Man. 'If the hag comes up with the ship, she will destroy every man of us.'

'She will not,' said Bowman. 'If I get one glimpse of that hag, I will put an end to her life; and do you listen, Hearing Ear, to know is she coming, and tell me when you hear her.'

'I hear her now,' said Hearing Ear. 'She is raging, and she is cursing

FIN MACCOOL, THE THREE GIANTS, AND THE SMALL MEN

those who were minding the children, and let them be taken. Now she is leaving the castle; now she is racing on after us.'

'Tell us, Far Feeler, when she is coming near,' said Fin.

'She is making a terrible uproar,' said Hearing Ear.

'She is coming toward us. She is very near,' said Far Feeler.

Bowman saw her, rested his bow on the shoulder of another, aimed, and sent an arrow through the one eye in the middle of the hag's forehead. She fell flat on the sea, and lay dead there. Fin and his small men moved forward swiftly to the castle. They arrived one hour before the end of night, and from that time till daybreak there was joy in the chamber. The small men and the two children of the king were playing together and enjoying themselves. Just before day, the king sent a servant to know what had happened in the chamber where his son was. The man could not enter, for they would not let him; but he looked through the keyhole. He went back then, and said to the king, –

'They seem to be very merry inside; and there are two lads in the room bigger than any of the small men.'

The king knew they would not be merry unless the child was there. What he did was to throw on his mantle, and go himself to see. He knocked at the door.

'Who is there?' asked Fin.

'I, – the king.'

The door was thrown open, and in walked the king. He saw the child in the cradle; but what was his wonder when he saw the other two. Without saying a word, he seized Fin's hand and shook it; and then he thanked him.

'There are your other two children,' said Fin; 'and do you know who stole them?'

'I do not.'

'I will tell you,' said Fin. 'Have you a sister?'

'I had,' answered the king, 'but we became enemies; and I know not where she is at this moment.'

Then Fin told everything that had happened in the night. 'And now you have your three sons,' said he to the king.

The king made a feast, which lasted seven days and seven nights. Never had there been such a feast in the kingdom of the Big Men as that; and sure why not, for wasn't it a great thing for the king to have his three sons home with him? When the feast was over, the king sent his men to carry all kinds of riches and treasures to Fin's ship; and for three days they were carrying them. At parting, the king said to Fin, 'If ever you need my assistance, you have only to send for it.'

Fin and his men sailed homeward then swiftly; and it was not long till they reached Fintra. The ship was unloaded; and Fin was glad, looking at his treasures, and thinking of his adventures in the land of the Big Men.

Some time after Fin had come from the land of the Big Men, he sent warriors to the chief ports of Erin to guard against enemies. One day his face was anxious and gloomy.

'You seem to be grieving,' said Dyeermud; 'you would better tell us what trouble is on you.'

'Some trouble is near me,' said Fin.

'By my hand,' said Oscar, 'if you do not tell me your trouble, I will not eat one morsel to-day.'

'Trouble is near me; but I know not yet what it is.'

'Chew your thumb then,' said Oscar.

Fin chewed his thumb from the flesh to the bone, from the bone to the marrow, from the marrow to the quick, and found out that there were three giants in the Eastern World who were coming to attack himself and his forces, drive them into the sea like sheep, and leave not a man of them living.

Fin knew not what to do; and he was in great grief that there should be three men who could invade all Erin, and destroy its defenders.

'Chew your thumb a second time,' said Oscar, 'to know is there any way to conquer them. We have travelled the world, and no people have the upper hand of us so far. There must be arms against these three.'

Fin chewed his thumb the second time; and the knowledge he got was this, that fire would not burn, water would not drown, swords would not cut either of the three giants. There was nothing to kill them but three things which their father had at home in the Eastern World;

FIN MACCOOL, THE THREE GIANTS, AND THE SMALL MEN

and if they saw those three things, they would fall dead, and dissolve into three heaps of jelly. What the three things were, was not told. 'Go now,' said Fin to Dyeermud, 'and find the forces, and I will watch myself for the enemy.'

Next morning Fin took his sword under his arm, went to Fintra, and began to herd bullocks. He did this for some time, till one day above another he saw three giants coming in toward him, the water not past their hips. He wasn't long waiting when they came near the cliff where he was; and he saw their hearts, their mouths were stretched open so widely, laughing at the boy herding the cattle.

'Where is Fin MacCool and his forces?' asked one of the giants.

'Well,' said Fin, 'it is not for me to tell you where Fin MacCool is; I am only his herder. But is there anything in the world to kill you? It must be there is not, and ye to have the courage to face Fin MacCool and his forces; for no people in the world have ever yet beaten them in battle.'

'We have come to Erin,' said the giants, 'to find Fin MacCool; and we will drive him and his forces into the sea, like sheep from the side of a mountain. Fire cannot burn us; swords do not cut us; and water will not drown us. Nothing in the world can cause our death but our own three caps; and where they are, neither you nor Fin will ever know.'

'How am I to know,' asked the herdsman, 'that fire will not burn you, or water drown you, or swords cut you? Let me give you a blow; and I'll know will swords cut you.'

'Oh, little man,' said one of the giants, 'how could you reach us with a sword?'

'I will show you a place,' said Fin, 'where I may be strong enough to give a blow ye would remember.'

He led the giants to a narrow place between two cliffs, and stood himself on the top of one cliff. He gave then a terrible blow of his sword to the head of one giant, but left not a sign of blood on him.

'By my hand!' said the giant, 'if every warrior in Fin MacCool's forces is as good at the sword as you, he need not be in dread of any men but us.'

Fin gave the second giant a terrible blow, and staggered him.

'Oh!' said the giant, 'no man ever gave me the like of that.'

He struck the third giant a blow, and knocked him to his knees; but not a drop of blood came.

'Such a blow as that,' said the giant, 'I never got from any man before. Now, how are you to know that water will not drown us?'

'There is a place which I will show you,' said Fin. 'If ye sleep in it to-night, and rise up in the morning before me, I shall know that water does not drown you.'

Fin showed a place where the water was twenty fathoms deep. The three lay down together under the water to stay till next morning. Fin hurried home then, gathered the Fenians together, and said, –

'I am in dread that these are the right giants. I knocked one trial out of them; swords will not cut them. They are sleeping to-night under twenty fathoms of water; but I am full sure that they will rise from it healthy and sound in the morning. Now, be ready, all of you, to scatter and go here and there throughout Erin. To-morrow, I am to try will fire burn them; when I know that, I will tell you what to do.'

The following morning, Fin went to where the giants had spent the night, and whistled. The three rose up to him at once, and came to land.

'Now,' said the eldest, as he looked around and saw the cattle, 'a bite to eat would not harm us.'

With that he faced one of the bullocks, and caught the beast by one horn.

'Leave him,' said Fin; 'you have no call to that bullock.'

Fin caught the bullock by the other horn. The giant pulled, and Fin held his own. One pulled, the other pulled, till between them they split the bullock from his muzzle to the tip of his tail, and made two equal parts of him.

''Tis a deal for me to have this much itself,' said Fin. 'I have saved half of my master's property. If ye want food, ye will get it at Fin's house. I will show the way; but first let me see will fire burn you.'

'Very well; we will make a great fire, and go into it; we'll stay in the fire till the wood is burned down, and then rise out of it as well as ever.'

There were many trees in the country at that time. The giants and Fin were not long making a great pile of dry limbs and logs. When the

FIN MACCOOL, THE THREE GIANTS, AND THE SMALL MEN

pile was finished, the giants sat on the top of it, and Fin brought fire. The flames rose as high as the tree-tops.

'''Tis too hot here for me,' said Fin.

'This is pleasant for us,' said the giants; and they laughed as Fin went from the heat.

Fin could not come within ten perches of the fire. It burned all day, and the blaze of it was seen all the following night. In the afternoon of the next day, the pile had burned down, and the three giants were sitting at their ease on the hot coals.

'Fire does not harm us; you see that,' said the giants.

'I do, indeed,' said Fin; 'and now ye may go to Fin's house for refreshment.'

Fin showed them a long road, hurried home himself by a short one, and gave command to the Fenians to scatter through Erin, and escape. Then, turning to his mother, he said, 'Make three cakes for the giants, put iron griddles in the middle of them, and bake them a little in the ashes. You will give these to the giants to eat. You will say that they are soft, not well baked; that we complain when the bread is not hard. I will lie down in the dark corner, in that big box there. Do you bind my head and face with a cloth, and say, when the giants are eating, "This poor child is sick; I think his teeth are coming."'

The old woman put three cakes in the ashes, and the griddles inside in them. When the giants came, the cakes were ready, and the old woman was sitting near the cradle.

'Is this Fin MacCool's house?' asked the giants.

'It is,' said the old woman.

'And is Fin himself in the house?'

'He is not then,' said the old woman; 'and it is seldom he is in it.'

'Have you any food to give us?'

'I have nothing but three loaves of bread; ye may have these, and welcome.'

'Give us the bread,' said the giants.

The old woman put the cakes on the table. One took a bite, another took a bite, then the third took a bite; and they all looked at one another.

'I know ye think the bread too soft,' said Fin's mother. 'The Fenians always blame me for making it too soft; and these cakes are not baked very well. They are softer than the usual bread of the Fenians.'

From shame, the giants ate the cakes, griddles and all. 'Well,' muttered they, 'to say that men would eat the like of that bread, and call it too soft! It is no wonder that they walked the world without finding their equals.'

'What exercise do the Fenians have after meals?' asked the giants.

'There is a stone outside,' said the old woman, 'which they throw over the house. They throw the stone, run in one door, run out the door opposite, and catch the stone before it comes to the earth.'

One giant caught the stone, but did not throw it. 'What is that?' said the other, running up and lifting the stone. To show his power, he threw it over the house, ran through both doors, and caught it coming down. The same giant threw the stone back again, and left it in its old place. Each of the others then did the same as the first. The life came near leaving Fin when he heard the giants throwing the stone, and racing to catch it. He was in dread they'd make bits of the house, and kill his old mother and himself.

'Oh, then,' said the giants, when they left the stone, 'it is no wonder that other people get no hand of the Fenians.'

'Well, old woman,' said the eldest giant, 'what is that you have there in the dark corner?'

'My grandson, and it is sick and peevish he is.'

'I suppose the child is getting his teeth?' said the giant.

'Indeed, then, I don't know,' said the old woman; 'but maybe it is the teeth that are troubling him.'

With that the eldest giant walked up to the cradle, and put his finger in the child's mouth; but if he did, Fin took two joints off his finger with a bite.

'Oh!' said the giant, 'if the child grows like that till he is a man, he will be the greatest champion in the world. To say that a child could take the finger off me, and he in the cradle!'

Away went the giants; and when they were gone, Fin called his eight small men, and hurried to the ship. They hoisted sails, and went. They raised gravel from the bottom of the sea, and put the foam of the waves in the place of the gravel; and with every bound the ship made, she went forward ten leagues. Never before did a ship cross the water so swiftly; and Fin never stopped till he anchored in the Eastern World. He put the fastenings of a day and a year on the ship, though he might not be absent one hour, and went away with his men. They were going on and travelling, and where did they come at last but to the castle of the old King of the Eastern World, the father of the three giants. The old king laughed when he saw Fin and the eight small men with him.

'In what part of the world do such people live, and where are you going?' asked the king. 'You would better stay with me till my three sons come home.'

'Where are your sons?' asked Fin.

'They are in Erin. They went to that country to bring me the head of Fin MacCool, and to drown all his forces in the deep ocean.'

'They must be great men,' said Fin, 'to go against Fin MacCool, and to think of drowning his forces, and bringing Fin's head to you. Do you know that no man ever got the better of Fin, or made any hand of the Fenians of Erin?'

'My sons are not like others,' said the king; 'but will you stay with me?'

'I will,' said Fin, 'and why not?'

The old king was very fond of amusement; and after a while Fin told what a wonderful archer one of his little boys was. The king appointed a day for a trial of skill in archery. All the greatest marksmen in the Eastern World were invited.

'Where does the king keep his sons' three caps?' asked Fin of Knowing Man.

'There is a secret chamber in the castle; no one here but the king knows where it is. In that chamber are the caps. The king always keeps the key of that chamber in his pocket.'

'You must show the chamber to Thief, to-morrow,' said Fin.

Next day, while the king was looking at the archery, and wondering at the skill of Bowman, who sent an arrow through the two eyes of a bird on the wing, Thief stole the key, and Knowing Man showed the secret chamber.

Thief stole the three caps, and gave them to Fin. Lazy Back ran for Bowman; and all were soon on the ship sailing for Erin as swiftly as they had come.

When the ship was near land in Erin, what should Fin see but all the Fenians coming down from the hilltops, and the three giants behind, driving them toward the water? He went to the top of the mast then, and raised the three caps on three sticks.

The giants looked at the vessel sailing in, and saw their own caps. That moment there was neither strength nor life left in them. They fell to the ground, and turned into three heaps of jelly. Fin had come just in season to rescue his forces; in another half hour, he would not have found a man of the Fenians alive in Erin.

'Oh, but you are here in time!' said Oscar.

'I am,' said Fin; 'and it is well for you that I was able to come.'

Fin and the Fenians had a great feast in Rahin, and a joyful night of it; and no wonder, for life is sweet.

Next day the time of the small men was out; and Fin went to the strand with them.

'I will pay you your wages to-day,' said Fin. 'To each man five gold-pieces. I am willing and glad to give more; for ye were the good servants to me.'

'We want nothing but our wages,' said the small men.

Fin paid each five gold-pieces. He wanted the ship in which he had sailed to the Eastern World, and kept his eye on it.

'Oh,' said Three Sticks, 'don't mind that ship; look at the one beyond.'

Fin turned in the other direction, and saw nothing but water.

'There is no ship there,' said he, turning to Three Sticks.

But Three Sticks and all his comrades were gone. Fin looked out on the water; the ship was gone too. He was sorry for the ship, and sorry for the small men; he would rather have them than all the Fenians of Erin.

FIN MACCOOL, CEADACH OG, AND THE FISH-HAG

On a time Fin MacCool and the Fenians were living at Rahonain, a mile distant from Fintra. While Fin and his men were near Fintra, a champion called Ceadach Og, son of the King of Sorach, came to them to learn feats of skill.

They received Ceadach with gladness; and after a time he learned all their feats, and departed. Fin and the Fenians were pleased with his company; and Ceadach was grateful to Fin and the Fenians.

At some distance from Fintra, there lived at that time a famed champion, who taught feats of valour and arms, and was surnamed the Knight of Instruction. With this man Ceadach engaged to gain still more knowledge.

The Knight of Instruction had a daughter; and there was with him a second man learning, whose nickname was Red Face.

When the champions had learned all the feats from the knight, the two were in love with his daughter. Not wishing that one of his pupils should envy the other, the knight could not settle which man to choose. He called then his druid, and laid the whole question before him.

'My advice,' said the druid, 'is this: Open two opposite doors in your castle; place your daughter half-way between them; and let the two champions pass out, one through one door, and one through the other. Whomever your daughter will follow, let her be the wife of that man.'

The champions had their own compact, that the man whom the young woman would follow should let the other have three casts of a spear at him, and he without right of defence; but if another would defend, he might let him.

The knight brought his daughter to the middle of the chamber, and opened the doors. The young woman went out after Ceadach.

Ceadach and his wife went their way then together; and he feared to stop at any place till he came to a great lonesome forest. He went to the middle of the forest, built a house there, and lived with his wife for a season.

One day as Fin was walking near the water at Fintra, he met a strange creature, – a woman to the waist, from the waist a fish. The human half was like an old hag. When Fin stopped before her, he greeted the hag. She returned the greeting, and asked him to play chess for a sentence.

'I would,' answered Fin, 'if I had my own board and chessmen.'

'I have a good board,' said the fish-hag.

'If you have,' said Fin, 'we will play; but if you win the first game, I must go for my own board, and you will play the second on that.'

The hag consented. They played on her chessboard, and the hag won that game.

'Well,' said Fin, 'I must go for my own board, and do you wait till I bring it.'

'I will,' said the fish-hag.

Fin brought his own board; and they played, and he won.

'Now,' said Fin, 'pass your sentence on me, since you won the first game.'

'I will,' said the hag; 'and I place you under sentence of weighty druidic spells not to eat two meals off the one table, nor to sleep two nights in the one bed, nor to pass out by the door through which you came in, till you bring me the head of the Red Ox, and an account of what took the eye from the Doleful Knight of the Island, and how he lost speech and laughter. Now pass sentence on me.'

'You will think it too soon when you hear it,' said Fin, 'but here it is for you. I place you under bonds of weighty druidic spells to stand on the top of that gable above there, to have a sheaf of oats fixed on the gable beyond you, and to have no earthly food while I'm gone,

FIN MACCOOL, CEADACH OG, AND THE FISH-HAG

except what the wind will blow through the eye of a needle fixed in front of you.'

'Hard is your sentence, O Fin,' said the fish-hag. 'Forgive me, and I'll take from your head my sentence.'

'Never,' said Fin. 'Go to your place without waiting.'

Before Fin departed, the fish hag had mounted the gable.

The fame of the Red Ox had spread through all lands in the world, and no man could go near him without losing life. The Fenians were greatly unwilling to face the Red Ox, and thought that no man could match him, unless, perhaps, Ceadach.

Though they knew not where Ceadach was living, nor where they were likely to find him, they started in search of that champion. They played with a ball, as they travelled, driving it forward before them, knowing that if Ceadach saw the ball he would give it a blow.

While passing the forest where Ceadach and his wife, the knight's daughter, were hiding, one of the Fenians gave the ball a great blow; but as he aimed badly, the ball flew to one side, went far away, and fell into the forest.

Ceadach was walking away from his house when the ball fell, and he saw it. He pulled down a tree-branch, and, giving a strong, direct blow, drove the ball high in the air, and out of the forest.

'No one struck that blow,' said the Fenians, 'but Ceadach, and he is here surely.' They went then toward the point from which they had seen the ball coming, and there they found Ceadach.

'A thousand welcomes, Fin MacCool,' said Ceadach. 'Where are you going?'

'I am under sentence to bring the head of the Red Ox; and 'tis for it that I am going: but I never can bring it unless you assist me. Without you, I cannot lift from my head the sentence that is on it.'

'If it lay with me, I would go with you gladly; but I know that my wife will not let me leave her. But do as I tell you now. When you come to us to eat dinner, taste nothing, and when my wife asks you to eat, say that you will not eat till she grants a request: if she will not grant it, leave the house, and let all the Fenians follow; if she grants you a request, you are to ask that I go with you. I know that she will grant you any request, except to take me in your company; for she is in dread that I may meet Red Face.'

They went to the house; the wife welcomed Fin with the others, and prepared dinner. When meat was placed before Fin, he would not taste it.

'Why not eat, O King of the Fenians?'

'I have a request to make. If you grant it, I will eat; if not, neither I nor my men will taste food.'

'Any request in my power, I will grant,' said she, 'except one.'

'What is that?' inquired Fin.

'If you want Ceadach to go with you, I'll not grant that.'

''Tis he that I want,' answered Fin.

'You'll not get him.'

'Well, you may keep him,' said Fin, rising from the table; and all the men followed. Conan Maol, who was with them, thought it hard to leave the dinner untasted, so he took a joint of meat with him.

When Fin and the Fenians had gone, Ceadach said to his wife, 'It is a great shame to us that Fin and the Fenians have left our house without tasting food, and this their first visit. Never can I face a man of the Fenians after what has happened this day.' And he talked till the wife consented to let him go with them.

Ceadach then whistled after Fin, who came back with his men; and they raised three shouts of joy when they heard that Ceadach would go with them. They entered the house then; all sat down to dinner, and they needed it badly.

After dinner, all set out together, and went to Ceadach's father, the King of Sorach, who was very powerful, and had many ships (Fin and the Fenians had no ships at that time). Ceadach's father had received no account of his son from the time that he left him at first, and was rejoiced at his coming.

Said Fin to the King of Sorach, 'I need a ship to bear me to the land where the Red Ox is kept.'

'You may take the best ship I have,' said the king.

Fin chose the best ship, and was going on board with his men when Ceadach's wife said to him, 'When coming back, you are to raise black sails if Ceadach is killed, but white sails if he is living.'

Fin commanded, and the men turned the prow to the sea, and the stern to land; they raised the great sweeping sails, and took their smoothly-polished ship past harbours with gently-sloping shores, and there the ship left behind it pale-green wavelets. Then a mighty wind swept through great flashing waves with such force that not a nail in the ship was left unheated, nor the finger of a man inactive; and the ship raised with its sailing a proud, haughty ridge in the sea. When the wind failed, they sat down with their oars of fragrant beech or white ash, and with every stroke they sent the ship forward three leagues through the water, where fishes, seals, and monsters rose around them, making music and sport, and giving courage to the men; and they never stopped nor cooled till they entered the chief port of the land where the Red Ox was kept.

When all had landed; Ceadach said, 'I need the fleetest man of the Fenians to help me against the Red Ox; and now tell me what each of you can do, and how fast he can run.'

'Let out,' said one man, 'twelve hares in a field with twelve gaps in it, and I will not let a hare out through any gap of the twelve.'

'Take a sieve full of chaff,' said a second man, 'to the top of a mountain; let the chaff go out with the wind; and I will gather all in again before as much as one bit of it comes to the ground.'

'When I run at full speed,' said a third man, 'my tread is so light that the dry, withered grass is not crushed underneath me.'

'Now, Dyeermud,' said Ceadach, 'I think that you were the swiftest of all when I was the guest of Fin MacCool and the Fenians of Erin; tell me, how swift are you now?'

'I am swifter,' said Dyeermud, 'than the thought of a woman when she is thinking of two men.'

'Oh, you will do,' said Ceadach; 'you are the fleetest of the Fenians; come with me.'

Fin and the Fenians remained near the ship, while Ceadach and Dyeermud went off to face the Red Ox.

The Red Ox's resting-place was enclosed by a wall and a hedge; outside was a lofty stone pillar; on this pillar the Red Ox used to rub his two sides. The Ox had but one horn, and that in the middle of his forehead. With that horn, which was four feet in length, he let neither fly, wasp, gnat, nor biting insect come near, and whatever creature came toward him, he sniffed from a distance.

When he sniffed the two champions, he rushed at them. Ceadach bounded toward the pillar.

Dyeermud took shelter at the hedge, and waited to see what would happen.

Ceadach ran round the pillar, and the Red Ox ran after him. Three days and three nights did they run; such was the speed of the two that Dyeermud never caught sight of them during that time, nor did they have sight of each other: the Red Ox followed by scent. Near the close of the third day, when both were growing tired, the Ox, seeing Ceadach, stopped for an instant to run across and pierce him with his horn. Dyeermud got a glimpse of the Ox, then rose in the air like a bird, split the forehead of the Ox with one blow, and stretched him.

'My love on your blow,' said Ceadach; 'and it was time for you to give it.'

'Purblindness and blindness to me,' replied Dyeermud, 'if I saw the Ox till that instant.'

Both were now joyful; for they had the head to take with them.

'If Fin and his men had this carcass,' said Dyeermud, 'it would give them beef for many a day.'

'Well, Dyeermud,' asked Ceadach, 'how much of the Ox can you carry?'

'I think I can take one quarter, with the head.'

'If you can do that,' said Ceadach, 'I'll take the rest of the carcass myself.'

Cutting off one quarter, he thrust through it the point of the horn, put the horn on Dyeermud's shoulder, with the head and quarter before and behind him. Ceadach took the other three quarters himself. Before they had gone half the way to the vessel, Dyeermud was tired, and Ceadach had to take that quarter as well as his own three; the head was as much as Dyeermud could carry.

When the two men appeared at the ship, all rejoiced greatly, and

FIN MACCOOL, CEADACH OG, AND THE FISH-HAG

welcomed them. Fin took the borabu then, and sounded it from joy; this sound could be heard through the world. As the report had gone to all regions that Fin was under sentence to kill the Red Ox, when Red Face heard the borabu, he said to himself, 'That is Fin; the Red Ox is killed; no one could kill him but Ceadach, and Ceadach is where the borabu is.' Red Face had the power of druidic spells; so he rose in the air, and soon dropped down near the Fenians, and was unseen till he stood there before them.

Said Red Face to Ceadach, ''Tis many a day that I am following you; you must stand your ground now.'

'What you ask is but fair,' answered Ceadach.

Red Face went to the distance of a spear's cast, and hurled his spear at Ceadach; but Dyeermud sprang up and caught it on his heel. Red Face made a second cast. Goll MacMorna raised his hand to stop the spear; but it went through his hand, and, going farther, pierced Ceadach, and killed him.

Red Face then vanished; and no man knew when he vanished, or to what place he went.

When Ceadach fell, the Fenians raised seven loud cries of grief that drove the badgers from the glens in which they were sleeping.

Said Dyeermud to Fin, 'Chew your thumb to know how we can bring Ceadach to life.'

Fin chewed his thumb from the skin to the flesh, from the flesh to the bone, from the bone to the marrow, from the marrow to the juice, and then he knew that there was a sow with three pigs in the Eastern World, and if blood from one of these pigs were put on Ceadach's wound, he would rise up well and healthy.

Fin took some men, and, leaving others to watch over Ceadach, set sail for the Eastern World, and never stopped till he anchored in a port near the place where the sow and her pigs were.

Fin knew all paths to the lair of the sow; and they went to it straightway. When they came, she was away hunting food; so they took the three pigs, hurried back to the vessel, set sail in all haste, and were soon out at sea. When the sow came back to her lair, it was empty. Then she found the scent of the men, followed it to the sea, and swam after the ship.

When the ship had made one-third of the voyage, the sow came in sight, and was soon near the stern. Fin ordered his men to throw out one pig of the three. The sow took the pig in her mouth, turned back, swam home, and left it in her lair. She turned a second time, followed the ship, and such was her speed and her venom, that little more than one-half of the voyage was over when the sow was in sight again. When near the ship, they threw her the second pig. The mother went back to her lair with the second pig, left it with the first, and rushed after the ship a third time. Land was in sight when they saw the sow raging on after them.

'Oh, we are lost!' cried the Fenians.

Dyeermud then took a bow with an arrow, and, resting the bow on another man's shoulder, aimed so truly at the widely-opened mouth of the sow, that the arrow, going in through her mouth, pierced her blood veins, and in no long time she turned her back downward and died.

They landed in safety, bled the pig; and when they let some of the blood into Ceadach's spear-wound, he sprang up alive.

When Ceadach was restored, Fin blew the borabu, and the Fenians raised seven shouts of joy that were heard throughout the whole kingdom. Then they set sail for Sorach.

Ceadach's wife thought her husband long in coming, and was watching and waiting every day for him. At last she saw the ship with white sails, and was glad.

Fin and his men landed, but left Ceadach on board.

'Where is Ceadach?' asked the wife, running out to meet Fin.

'He is dead on the vessel,' said Fin.

'Why did you not raise black sails as you promised?'

'We were so troubled that we forgot it.'

'It was well for you to forget; for if you had raised black sails, I should have drowned every man of you.'

'Ceadach is living and well; have no fear,' said Fin, and he sounded the borabu.

Ceadach landed. His father and wife were so glad to see him that they feasted Fin and the Fenians for seven days and seven nights.

Fin told Ceadach's wife of all their adventures, and what struggles they had in bringing her husband to life. She was glad; for the trouble with Red Face was ended.

Ceadach went now with Fin to visit the Doleful Knight of the Island; and they never halted nor stopped till they came to his castle.

Fin found the knight sitting at a great heavy table, his head on his hand, his elbow on the table, into which it had worn a deep hole; a stream of tears was flowing from his eye to the table, and from the table to the floor.

'A hundred thousand welcomes to you, Fin MacCool,' said the knight; and he began to weep more than ever. 'I was once in prosperity, and at that time this was a pleasant place for a good man to visit; but now it is different. I have food in plenty, but no one to cook it.'

'If that's all your trouble,' said Fin, 'we can cure it.'

Fin's men were not slow in preparing a dinner. When the dinner was eaten, the knight turned to Fin and inquired, 'Why have you come to my castle, Chief of the Fenians of Erin?'

'I will tell you,' said Fin. Then he related his story, and all his adventures with Ceadach.

'Well,' said the knight, 'it will shorten my life by seven years to give the tale of my sufferings; for they will be as fresh to me now, as when first I went through them. But as you are under bonds to know them, I will tell you.

'I was here in wealth and prosperity, myself and my three sons. We used to hunt beasts and birds with our dogs when it pleased us. On a May morning a hare came, and frisked before my hall-door. Myself and my three sons then followed her with dogs, and followed all day till the height of the evening. Then we saw the hare enter an old fairy fort. The opening was wide; we were able to follow. In we rushed, all of us, and the next thing we saw was a fine roomy building. We went in, looked around for the hare, but saw not a sight of her. There was no one within but an old man and woman. We were not long inside till three gruagachs came, each with a wild boar on his shoulders. They threw the wild boars on the floor, and told me to clean them, and cook them for dinner. One of my sons fell to cleaning a boar; but for every hair that he took from him, ten new ones came out, so the sooner he stopped work the better.

'Then one of the old gruagach's sons placed the boars in a row, the head of the one near the tail of the other, and, taking a reed, blew once, the hair was gone from all three; twice, the three boars were dressed; a third time, all were swept into one caldron.

'When the meal was cooked and ready, a gruagach brought two spits to me, one of dull wood, the other formed of sharp iron. The old man asked, "Which will you choose?"

'I chose the sharp iron spit, went to the caldron, and thrust in the spit; but if I did, I raised only a poor, small bit of meat, mostly bone. That was what I and my three sons had for dinner.

'After dinner, the old man said, "Your sons may perform now a feat for amusement."

'In three rooms were three cross-beams, as high from the floor as a man's throat. In the middle of each beam was a hole. Through this hole passed a chain, with a loop at each end of it. In front of the hole on each side of the beam was a knife, broad and sharp. One loop of each chain was put on the neck of a son of mine, and one on the neck of a gruagach. Then each of the six was striving to save his own throat, and to cut off the head of the other man; but the gruagachs pulled my three sons to the cross-beams, and took the three heads off them.

'Then they dressed them, and boiled them for supper. When that supper was ready, they struggled to force me to eat some, but could not. Next they threw me across the broad table, plucked out one eye from my head, thrust a light in the socket, and made me lie there, and serve as a candlestick. In the morning, I was flung out through the door, while the gruagach cried after me, "You'll not come to this castle a second time!"'

'Have you seen that hare since?' inquired Ceadach.

'I have, for she comes each May morning, and that renews and gives strength to my sorrow.'

'To-morrow will be May day; come with me, and we'll hunt her,' said Ceadach.

'I will not,' said the Knight of the Island.

The hare came after breakfast next morning, and halted in front

FIN MACCOOL, CEADACH OG, AND THE FISH-HAG

of the castle. The knight was unwilling to hunt, but still yielded to Ceadach, and followed with the others.

Time after time, they came close to the hare, but never could catch her. At last, in the height of the evening, when nearing the same fairy fort, the hound Bran snapped at the haunch of the hare, and took a full bite from her. All passed through the entrance, found the house, and no person inside but an old man and woman. The old woman was lying in bed, and she groaning.

'Have you seen a hare in this house?' inquired Ceadach.

'I have not,' said the old man.

Ceadach saw traces of blood on the bed, and went toward the old woman, who was covered up closely; raising the clothes, he said, 'Maybe 'tis here that the hare is.'

The old woman was covered with blood, and wounded in the very same way as the hare. They knew then who was the cause of misfortune to the Knight of the Island, and who made the visits each year on May morning.

They were not long in the house when the gruagachs, the sons of the old man, came in, each with a wild boar on his shoulders. Seeing the Knight of the Island, they laughed, and said, 'We thought you had enough of this place the first time that you came here.'

'I saw more than I wished to see,' said the Knight of the Island; 'but I had to come this time.'

'Have you any man to cook dinner for us?' asked the old gruagach of Fin.

'I'll do that myself,' put in Ceadach, who turned to one of the brothers, and asked, 'Where is your reed; I must use it.'

The reed was brought. Ceadach blew once, the boars were clean; twice, they were dressed, and ready; thrice, they were in the caldron.

When the spits were brought, Ceadach took the dull wooden spit, thrust it into the pot, and took up all that was in there.

Fin, Ceadach, and the knight ate to their own satisfaction; then they invited the old gruagach and his three sons to dinner.

'What amusement have you in this place?' asked Fin, later in the evening.

'We have nothing,' said the old gruagach and his sons.
'Where are your chains?' asked Ceadach.
'We make no use of them now,' said the young gruagachs.
'You must bring them,' said Ceadach.

The chains were brought, drawn through the cross-beams, and three loops of them put on the necks of the gruagachs. No matter what strength was in the three brothers, nor how they struggled, Ceadach brought their throats to the knives, and took the three heads off them. Next they were boiled in the caldron, as the knight's three sons had been boiled the first time. Then Ceadach seized the old gruagach, flung him across the broad table, plucked out one eye from his head, and fixed a light in the empty socket.

At sight of what the gruagachs passed through, the Doleful Knight of the Island let one roaring laugh out of him, his first laugh in seven years.

Next morning Ceadach, pointing to the Knight of the Island, said to the old gruagach, 'Unless you bring this man's three sons to life, I will take your own head from you.'

The bones of the three sons were in three heaps of dust outside the door. The gruagach took a rod of enchantment, and struck the bones. The three sons of the knight rose up as well and strong as ever, and went home. The Knight of the Island gave a feast to Fin and Ceadach. After that Fin, with his men and Ceadach, sailed back to the King of Sorach. Ceadach remained with his wife and father. Fin went to the harbour of Fintra, taking with him the head of the Red Ox, and the story of the Doleful Knight, to the fish-hag.

'Have you the head of the Red Ox?' asked the hag.
'I have,' answered Fin.
'You will give it to me,' said the hag.
'I will not,' answered Fin. 'If I was bound to bring it, I was not bound to give it.'

When she heard that, the hag dropped to the earth, and became a few bones.

FIN MACCOOL, FAOLAN, AND THE MOUNTAIN OF HAPPINESS

When Fin MacCool and the Fenians of Erin were at Fintra, they went hunting one day; and the man who killed the first deer was Dyeermud. When the hunt was over, they returned to the place where the first deer was started, and began, as was usual, to prepare the day's feast. While preparing the feast, they saw a ship sailing into the harbour, with only one woman on board. The Fenians were greatly surprised at the speed of the vessel; and Dyeermud said to Fin, 'I will go and see who is the woman coming in that vessel.'

'You killed the first deer,' replied Fin, 'and the honours of the feast on this day are yours. I myself will go down and see who the woman is.'

The woman cast anchor, sprang ashore, and saluted Fin, when he came to the strand. Fin returned the salute, and, after a while, she asked, 'Will you play a game of chess for a sentence?'

'I will,' answered Fin.

They played, and she won.

'What is your sentence on me?' inquired Fin.

'I sentence you, under bonds of heavy enchantment,' said she, 'to take me for your wife.'

Fin had to marry the woman. After a time, she said, 'I must leave you now for a season.'

Fin drove his sword then, with one mighty blow, into a tree-stump, and said, 'Call your son Faolan [little wolf], and never send him to me until he is able to draw the sword from this stump.'

She took the stump with her, and sailed away homeward. She nursed her son for only three days, and preserved the rest of the milk for a different use. The boy was called Faolan, was trained well in the use of all arms, and when ten years of age, he was skilled beyond any master. One day there was a game of hurley, and Faolan played alone, against twenty one others. The rule of that game was that whoever won was to get three blows of his club on each one who played against him. Faolan gave three blows to each of the twenty-one men; among them was one who was very much hurt by the blows, and he began to say harsh words to Faolan, and added, 'You don't know your own father.'

Faolan was greatly offended at this. He went home to his mother, in tears, and asked, 'Who is my father? I will never stop nor stay till I find him.'

'What caused your vexation?' asked the mother. 'Why do you ask such a question at this time?'

Faolan told her the words of the player. At last she said, 'Your father is Fin MacCool, Chief of the Fenians of Erin; but you are not to be sent to him till you can draw his sword from the tree-stump into which he drove it with one blow.'

'Show me the sword and the tree-stump,' said Faolan.

She took him then to the stump. With one pull, he drew out the sword.

'Prepare me food for the road,' said Faolan. 'I will go to my father.'

The mother made ready three loaves of bread, kneaded them with the milk which she had saved, and baked them.

'My son,' said she, 'do not refuse bread on the journey to any one whom you meet; give it from these loaves, even should you meet your worst enemy.'

She took down a sword then, gave it to him, and said, 'This was your grandfather's sword; keep it, and use it till a better one comes to you.'

Faolan took a blessing of his mother, set out on his journey, and was walking always, till he came to a harbour where he found a ship bound for Erin. He went on board, and was not sailing long, when a venomous hound rose up in the sea, and cast such high waves at the vessel as to throw it back a long distance.

FIN MACCOOL, FAOLAN, AND THE MOUNTAIN OF HAPPINESS

Remembering his mother's advice about sharing the bread, Faolan threw one loaf to the hound. This seemed to appease him. He had not sailed much further, when the hound rose again. Faolan threw out the second loaf; and the beast disappeared for a while, but rose the third time, and drove back the vessel. Faolan threw the third loaf; and, after disappearing the third time, the hound rose the fourth time. Having nothing to give, Faolan seized a brazen ball which his mother had given him, and, hurling it at the hound with good aim, killed him on the spot. As soon as the hound fell, there rose up a splendid youth, who came on board, and, shaking Faolan's hand, said, –

'I thank you; you delivered me from enchantment. I am your mother's brother; and there was nothing to free me till I ate three loaves kneaded with your mother's milk, and was then killed by you with that brazen ball. You are near Ventry Strand now; among the first men you meet will be your own father. You will know him by his dress; and when you meet him, kneel down and ask for his blessing. As I have nothing else to give, here is a ring to wear on your finger, and whenever you look at it you will feel neither cold, thirst, nor hunger.'

When they landed, the uncle went his own way and vanished. Faolan saw champions playing on the strand, throwing a great weighty sledge.

Knowing Fin from his mother's description, he knelt down at his feet, and asked for his blessing.

'If you are a son of mine,' said Fin, 'you are able to hurl this sledge.'

'He is too young,' said Dyeermud, 'to throw such a weight; and it is a shame for you to ask him to throw it.'

The youth then, growing angry, caught the sledge, and hurled it seven paces beyond the best man of the Fenians.

Fin shook hands with the youth; and his heart grew big at having such a son. Dyeermud shook his hand also, and swore that as long as he lived he would be to him a true comrade.

When dinner-time came, Fin bade Faolan sit down at his right hand, where Conan Maol, son of Morna, sat usually. Fin gave this place to Conan to keep him in humor. Conan grew enraged now, and said, 'It is great impudence for a stripling to sit in my place.'

'I know not who you are,' said Faolan, 'but from what I hear you must be Conan Maol, who has never a good word for any man; and I would break your head on the wall, but I don't wish to annoy people present.'

It was a custom of the Fenians in eating to set aside every bone that had marrow for Oscar, and as Faolan had a thick marrow-bone in his hand, he began to pick out the marrow, and eat it. This enraged Oscar, and he said, 'You must put that bone aside as the others put their bones; that is my due, and I will have it.'

'As the meat is mine,' said Faolan, 'so is the marrow.'

Oscar snatched at the youth, and caught the bone by one end. Faolan held the other end. Both pulled till they broke the bone, then, seizing each other, they went outside for a struggle. As the two were so nearly related, the other men stopped them. Fin took Oscar aside then, and asked, 'How long could you live if we let the youth keep his grip on you?'

'If he kept his grip with the same strength, I could not live five minutes longer.'

Fin took Faolan aside then, and asked the same question.

'I could live for twelve months, if he squeezed me no tighter.'

The two then kept peace with each other. All were very fond of Faolan, especially Dyeermud, who was a good, loyal comrade; and he warned Faolan to distrust and avoid Grainne, Fin's wife, as much as he could. The youth was learning, meanwhile, to practise feats of activity and bravery. At the end of twelve months, the Fenians were setting out on a distant hunt, for which they had long been preparing. On the eve of the hunt, Grainne dropped on her knees before Fin, and begged him to leave Faolan with her for company, until he and the rest would return. Fin consented, and Faolan stayed with Grainne.

When all the others had gone to the great hunt, Faolan and Grainne went also to hunt in the neighbourhood. They did not go far, and returned. After dinner, Grainne asked Faolan would he play a game of chess for a small sentence. He said that he would. They played, and he won.

'What is your sentence on me?' asked Grainne.

'I have no sentence at this time,' replied Faolan.

FIN MACCOOL, FAOLAN, AND THE MOUNTAIN OF HAPPINESS

They played again, and she won.

'Now put your sentence on me,' said the youth.

'You will think it soon enough when you hear it. You are not to eat two meals off the same table, nor sleep two nights on the same bed, till you bring me the tallow of the three oxen on Sliav Sein [Mountain of Happiness].'

When he heard this sentence, he went off, threw himself face downward on his bed, and remained there without eating or drinking till the Fenians came back from the hunt. Fin and Dyeermud, not seeing Faolan when they came, went in search of him.

'Have you found Faolan?' asked Dyeermud of Fin, when he met him soon after.

'I have not,' answered Fin.

Dyeermud then went to see if he could find Faolan in bed. As the door of his chamber was fastened, and no one gave answer, Dyeermud forced it, and found Faolan on his face in the bed. After they had greeted each other, Faolan told of the trouble that was on him.

'I gave you warning against Grainne,' said Dyeermud; 'but did you win any game of her?'

'I did; but have put no sentence on her yet.'

'I am glad,' answered Dyeermud; 'and let me frame the sentence. I swear by my sword to be loyal to you; and where you fall, I will fall also. But be cheerful, and come to the feast.'

They went together, and Fin, seeing them, was glad. He knew, however, that something had happened to Faolan. Dyeermud went to Fin, and told him of the mishap to the youth. Fin was troubled at what had come on his son.

'I have sworn,' said Dyeermud, 'to follow Faolan wherever he may be.'

'I will send with him,' said Fin, 'the best man of the Fenians.'

Dyeermud, Oscar, and Goll, son of Morna, were summoned.

'What is your greatest feat?' inquired Fin of Goll.

'If I were to stand in the middle of a field with my sword in my hand on the rainiest day that ever rose, I could keep my head dry with my sword, not for that day alone, but for a day and a year,' answered Goll.

'That is a good feat,' said Fin. 'What is your greatest feat, Oscar?'

'If I open a bag filled with feathers on a mountain-top of a stormy day, and let the feathers fly with the wind, the last feather will barely be out of the bag, when I will have every feather of them back into the bag again.'

'That is a very good feat,' answered Fin, 'but it is not enough yet. Now, Dyeermud, what is your feat of swiftness?'

'If I were put on a space of seven hundred acres, and each acre with a hedge around it, and there were seven hundred gaps in the hedge of each acre, and seven hundred hares were put on each acre of the seven hundred, I would not let one hare out of the seven hundred acres for a day and a year.'

'That is a great feat,' remarked Fin; 'that will do.'

'Chew your thumb, O Fin,' said Dyeermud, 'and tell me if it is fated to us to come back from the journey?'

Fin chewed his thumb. 'You will come back; but the journey will be a hard and a long one: you will be ankle deep in your own blood.'

Dyeermud went to Faolan, and told him what sentence to put upon Grainne.

On the following day, Fin led Grainne forth for her sentence; and Faolan said, 'You are to stand on the top of Sliav Iolar [Mount Eagle], till I come back to Fintra; you are to hold in your hand a fine needle; you are to have no drink saving what rain you can suck through the eye of that needle, no food except what oats will be blown through the eye of that very needle from a sheaf on Sliav Varhin; and Dyeermud will give three blows of a flail to the sheaf to loosen the grain.'

Faolan and Dyeermud set out on their journey. They travelled three days, and saw no house in which they could rest for the night.

'When we find a house,' said Dyeermud, 'we will have from the people a lodging, either with their good will, or in spite of them.'

'I will help you in that,' said Faolan.

On the evening of the fourth day, a large white-fronted castle appeared in the distance. They went toward it, and knocked at the door. A fine young woman welcomed them kindly, and kissed Faolan. 'You and I,' said she, 'were born at the same hour, and betrothed at our birth.

FIN MACCOOL, FAOLAN, AND THE MOUNTAIN OF HAPPINESS

Your mother married Fin to rescue her brothers, your uncles, from the bonds of enchantment.'

They sat down to eat and drink, the young woman, Dyeermud, and Faolan; they were not long eating when in came four champions, all torn, cut, and bleeding. When Dyeermud saw these, he started up, and seized his sword.

'Have no fear,' said the young woman to Dyeermud.

'We are returning from battle with a wild hag in the neighbourhood,' said the four champions. 'She is trying to take our land from us; and this is the seventh year that we are battling with the hag. All of her warriors that we kill in the daytime, she raises at night; and we have to fight them again the next day.'

'No man killed by my sword revives; and these will not, if I kill them,' said Dyeermud.

'They would revive after your sword,' said the four champions.

'Do you stay at home to-morrow,' said Dyeermud; 'Faolan and I will give battle to the hag and her forces; no one whom we slay will trouble you hereafter.'

The four champions agreed, and gave every direction how to find the wild hag and her army. Faolan and Dyeermud went to the field; one began at one end, and one at the other, and fought till they met in the middle at sunset, and slew all the hag's warriors.

'Go back to the castle,' said Faolan to Dyeermud; 'I will rest here to-night, and see what gives life to the corpses.'

'I will stay,' replied Dyeermud, 'and you may return.'

'No, I will stay here,' said Faolan; 'if I want help, I will run to the castle.'

Dyeermud went back to the castle. About midnight, Faolan heard the voice of a man in the air just above him. 'Is there any one living?' asked the voice. Faolan, with a bound, grasped the man, and, drawing him down with one hand, pierced him through with a sword in his other hand. The man fell dead; and then, instead of the old man that he seemed at first, he rose up a fresh young man of twenty two years. The young man embraced and thanked Faolan. 'I am your uncle,' said he, 'brother of the poisonous hound that you freed from enchantment at sea. I was fourteen years in the power of the wild hag, and could not be freed till my father's sword pierced me. Give me that sword which belonged to my father. It was to deliver me that your mother gave you that blade. I will give you a better one still, since you are a greater champion than I. I will give you my grandfather's sword; here it is. When the wild hag grows uneasy at my delay, she herself will hasten hither. She knew that you were to come and release me, and she is preparing this long time to meet you. For seven years, she has been making steel nails to tear you to pieces; and she has sweet music which she will play when she sees you: that music makes every man sleep when he hears it. When you feel the sleep coming, stab your leg with your sword; that will keep you awake. She will then give you battle; and if you chance to cut off her head, let not the head come to the body: for if it comes on the body, all the world could not take it away. When you cut off her head, grasp it in one hand, and hold it till all the blood flows out; make two halves of the head, holding it in your hand all the while; and I will remove the stone cover from a very deep well here at hand; and do you throw the split head into that well, and put the cover on again.'

The uncle went aside then; and soon the hag came through the air. Seeing Faolan, she began to play strains of beautiful music, which were putting him to sleep; but he thrust his new sword in the calf of his leg, and kept away sleep. The wild hag, outwitted, attacked the youth fiercely, and he went at her in earnest. Every time that she caught him with her nails, she scraped skin and flesh from his head to his heels; and then, remembering his mother, and being aroused by his uncle, he collected his strength, and with one blow cut the head off the hag; but he was so spent from the struggle that it took him some time to seize the head, and so weak was he that he could not raise his hand to split it.

'Lay your sword on the head; the blade alone will split it!' cried the uncle.

Faolan did this. The sword cut the head; and then Faolan threw the head into the well. Just as he was going to cover the well, the head spoke, and said, 'I put you under bonds of heavy enchantment not to eat two meals off the same table, nor sleep two nights on the same bed,

FIN MACCOOL, FAOLAN, AND THE MOUNTAIN OF HAPPINESS

till you tell the Cat of Gray Fort that you destroyed the wild hag out of her kingdom.'

The uncle embraced Faolan then, and said, 'Now I will go to my sister, your mother; but first I will guide you to this hag's enchanted well: if you bathe in its water, you will be as sound and well as ever.'

Faolan went, bathed in the well, and, when fully recovered, returned to the castle. Thinking Gray Fort must be near by, he did not rouse Dyeermud, but went alone in search of the cat. He travelled all day, and at last saw a great fort with the tail of a cat sticking out of it. 'This may be the cat,' thought he, and he went around the whole fort to find the head. He found it thrust out just beyond the tail.

'Are you the Cat of Gray Fort?' inquired Faolan.

'I am,' said the cat.

'If you are,' said Faolan, 'I destroyed the wild hag out of her kingdom.'

'If you did,' said the cat, 'you will kill no one else; for the hag was my sister.'

The cat rushed at Faolan then; and, bad as the hag had been, the cat was far worse. The two fought that night furiously, till the following morning, when Faolan cut the cat in two halves across the middle. The half that the head was on ran around trying to meet the other half; but before it could do so, Faolan cut the head off the front half. Then the head spoke, and said, –

'I put you under bonds of enchantment not to eat two meals off the one table, nor sleep two nights on the one bed, till you tell the Kitten of Cul MacKip that you killed the Cat of Gray Fort and destroyed the wild hag out of her kingdom.'

Faolan then hurried forward to find the kitten. Thinking that her place was near, he did not go back to the castle for Dyeermud, but held on the whole day, walking always. Toward evening, he saw a castle, went toward it, and entered it. When inside he saw half a loaf of barley-bread and a quart of ale placed on the window. 'Whoever owns these, I will use them,' said the youth.

When he had eaten and drunk, he put down a fire for the night, and saw a kitten lying near the ashes. 'This may be the Kitten of Cul

MacKip,' thought he; and, shaking it, he asked, 'Are you the Kitten of Cul MacKip?'

'I am,' said the kitten.

'If you are,' said Faolan, 'then I tell you that I killed the Cat of Gray Fort and destroyed the wild hag out of her kingdom.'

'If you did,' said the kitten, 'you will never kill any one else,' and, starting up, the kitten stretched, and was as big as a horse in a moment. She sprang at Faolan, and he at her. They fought fiercely that night, and the following day, but Faolan, toward evening, swept the head off the kitten; but as he did, the head spoke, and said, 'I put you under bonds of heavy enchantment not to eat two meals off the same table, nor sleep two nights on the same bed, till you tell the Dun Ox that you slew the Kitten of Cul MacKip, killed the Cat of Gray Fort, and destroyed the wild hag out of her kingdom.'

Before setting out, Faolan saw a brass ball on the window, and, taking it, said to himself, 'I may kill some game with this on the road.'

Away he went then, and walked on till he came to where the road lay through a wood; near the road was a forester's cabin. Out came the forester with a hundred thousand welcomes.

'Glad am I to see you; gladder still would I be if your comrade, Dyeermud, were with you,' said the forester.

'Can you tell me where the Dun Ox is?' asked Faolan.

'In this wood,' said the forester; 'but do you bring your comrade to help you against the Dun Ox; by no chance can you slay him alone. The Dun Ox has only one eye, and that in the middle of his forehead; over that eye is a shield of white metal; from that shield two bars of iron run back to the tail of the ox. Behind him, two champions are on guard always; and when any one nears him, the ox sniffs the stranger, and roars; the champions lean on the bars then, and raise up the shield. When the one eye of the ox sees the person approaching, that moment the person falls dead. What are your chances of slaying that ox? Go back for your comrade.'

'I will not,' said Faolan; 'the ox will fall by me, or I by the ox.'

'It is you that will fall,' said the forester.

Faolan entered the cabin, where the forester treated him well. Next morning the forester showed the path that lay toward the place where the ox was. Faolan had not gone far when the ox roared, and, looking in the direction of the roar, he saw the two champions just seizing the bars to raise up the shield, so, failing other means, he sent the ball, with a well-aimed cast, and crushed in the forehead of the ox through the shield. The ox fell dead, but, before falling, his eye turned on Faolan, who dropped dead also.

Dyeermud slept a hero's sleep of seven days and seven nights. When he woke, and found no tidings of Faolan, he was furious; but the four champions calmed him; and the young woman said, 'The wild hag may have killed him; but if as much as one bone of his body can be found, I will bring him to life again.'

Dyeermud, Faolan's betrothed, and her four brothers set out, and, coming to the battle-field, found the army of the wild hag slain, but no trace of Faolan. They went to the well then, and saw the split head there.

The six went to Gray Fort, and found the cat dead, the hind-part in one place, the fore-part in a second, and the head in a third.

'The head must have sent him to the Kitten of Cul MacKip,' said the young woman; 'that kitten has twice as much witch power as the cat and the old hag; all three are sisters.'

They went farther, and, finding the kitten dead, went to find the Dun Ox; 'for Faolan must be dead near him,' said the young woman. When they came to his cabin, the forester greeted them, and gave a hundred thousand welcomes to Dyeermud, who was surprised, and inquired, 'How do you know me? I have never been in this country before.'

'I know you well; for I saw you two years ago in combat with the Champion of the Eastern World on Ventry Strand. Many persons were looking at that combat, but you did not see them. I was there with the others.'

'Have you seen a young champion pass this way?' asked Dyeermud.

'I have,' said the forester; 'but he must have perished by the Dun Ox, for I have not heard the ox bellow this long time.'

The six spent that night at the forester's cabin; and, setting out next morning early, they soon found Faolan. The young woman bathed him with some fluid from a vial, and, opening his mouth, poured the rest down his throat. He rose up at once, as sound and healthy as ever. All went to the ox, which they found lying dead, and the two champions also; and, searching about, they found the brazen ball sunk in the earth some distance away. Faolan took it up carefully. They went back to the forester's cabin, and enjoyed themselves well.

'Do you know where the Mountain of Happiness is?' inquired Dyeermud of the forester, during the night.

'I do not,' said the forester; 'but I know where the Black-Blue Giant lives, and he knows every place in the world. That giant has never given a meal or a night's lodging to any man. He has an only daughter, who is in love with you, since she saw you two years ago in combat with the Champion of the Eastern World on Ventry Strand, although you did not see her. This daughter is closely confined by the giant, fearing she may escape to you; and if you succeed in reaching her, she is likely to know, if her father knows, where the Mountain of Happiness is.'

'How did you get tidings of the giant's daughter?' asked Dyeermud.

'I will not tell you now,' said the forester, 'but I will go with you to guide you to the giant, and I may give you assistance. Here are three keys, – the keys of the castles of the Dun Ox, of the Kitten of Cul MacKip, and of the Cat of Gray Fort; they are yours now.'

'Those keys are not mine,' said Dyeermud; 'they belong to Faolan, who slew the three owners.'

'If Faolan slew them,' said the forester, 'he had assistance, which caused you to come to him.'

'Keep the keys till we come back,' said Dyeermud.

The seven travelled on then, and were going ten days when they saw the giant's castle. Now this castle stood on one leg, and whirled around always.

'I will use my strength on that castle, to know can I stop it,' said Dyeermud.

'You cannot stop it,' said the forester. 'I will stop it myself. Do you watch the door of the castle, which is on the top of the roof, and, when the castle stops, spring in through the door, and seize the giant, if he is inside, and compel him to give a night's lodging.'

FIN MACCOOL, FAOLAN, AND THE MOUNTAIN OF HAPPINESS

The forester then made for the castle, and, placing his shoulder against one of the corners, kept it standing still; and Dyeermud, leaping in by the roof, came down before the giant, who had started up, knowing something was wrong when the castle stood still.

Dyeermud and the giant grappled each other so fiercely, and fought with such fury, that the castle was shivering. The giant's wife begged them to go out of the castle, and fight on the open, and not frighten the life out of herself and the child in her arms.

Out went the Black-Blue Giant and Dyeermud, and fought until Dyeermud brought down the giant and sprained his back. The giant let a roar out of him, and begged there for quarter.

'Your head is mine,' answered Dyeermud.

'It is,' said the giant; 'but spare me, and I will give you whatever you ask for.'

'I want lodging for myself and my company.'

'You will get that,' said the giant.

All then went into the giant's castle; and when they were sitting at dinner, Dyeermud ate nothing.

'Why is this?' asked the giant.

'It is the custom of the Fenians of Erin,' said he, 'not to eat at a table where all the members of the house are not present.'

'All my people are here,' said the giant.

'They are not,' answered Dyeermud; 'you have one daughter not present.'

The giant had to bring the daughter. They ate then. The forester talked after dinner with Dyeermud, and said, 'The giant's daughter has a maid; you must bribe her to give you the key of her mistress's chamber; and if you come by the young woman's secrets, she may tell you where the Mountain of Happiness is, if she knows.'

Dyeermud went to the maid. 'You will not be here always,' said he; 'your mistress will marry me, and leave this castle; then you'll have no business here. I will take you with us if you give me the key of the chamber.'

'The giant himself keeps that key under his pillow at night; he sleeps only one nap, like a bird, but sleeps heavily that time. If you promise to take me with my mistress, I'll strive to bring the key hither.'

'I promise,' said Dyeermud.

The maid brought the key, and gave it on condition that she was to have it again within an hour. Dyeermud went then to the giant's daughter, and when her first wonder was over, he asked, 'Do you know where the Mountain of Happiness is?'

'I do not. My father knows well, but for some reason he has never told me, so he must have fared very badly there; but if you lay his head on a block, and threaten to cut it off with your sword, he will tell you, if you ask him; but otherwise he will not tell.'

'I will do that; and I will take you to Erin when I go,' answered Dyeermud.

'Where is the Mountain of Happiness?' asked Dyeermud of the giant, next morning.

He would not tell. Dyeermud caught the giant, who could not resist him on account of his sprained back; he drew him out, placed his head on a block, and said, 'I will cut the head off you now, unless you tell me what you know of the Mountain of Happiness. The Fenians of Erin have but the one word, and it is useless for you to resist me; you must go with us, and show us the way to the mountain.'

The giant, finding no escape possible, promised to go. They set out soon, taking all the arms needed. As the mountain was not far distant, they reached the place without great delay. The giant showed them the lair of the oxen, but after a promise that he should be free to escape should danger threaten.

'I know all the rest now,' said the forester. 'Do you,' said he to Dyeermud, 'stand straight in front of the lair, and I, with Faolan, will stand with drawn swords, one on each side of the entrance; and do you,' said he to the four brothers, 'knock down the entrance, and open the place for the oxen to rush out. If the head of each ox is not cut off when he stands in the entrance, the world would not kill him from that out.'

All was done at the forester's word. The entrance was not long open, when out rushed an ox; but his head was knocked off by the forester. Faolan slew the second ox; but the third ox followed the second so quickly that he broke away, took Dyeermud on his horns, and went like

FIN MACCOOL, FAOLAN, AND THE MOUNTAIN OF HAPPINESS

a flash to the top of the Mountain of Happiness. This mountain stood straight in front of the lair, but was far away. On the mountain, the ox attacked Dyeermud; and they fought for seven days and nights in a savage encounter. At the end of seven days, Dyeermud remembered that there was no help for him there, that he was far from his mother and sister, who were all he had living, and that if he himself did not slay the fierce ox, he would never see home again; so, with one final effort, he drove his sword through the heart of the ox. He himself was so spent from the struggle and blood-loss that he fainted, and would have died on the mountain, but for his companions, who came now. They were seven days on the road over which the ox passed in a very few minutes.

The forester rubbed Dyeermud with ointment, and all his strength came to him. They opened the ox, took out all the tallow, and, going back to the other two oxen, did in like manner, saving the tallow of each of them separately. They went next to the castle of the Black-Blue Giant.

'Will you set out for home to-morrow?' asked the forester, turning to Dyeermud.

'We will,' answered Dyeermud.

'Oh, foolish people!' said the forester. 'Those three oxen were brothers of Grainne, and were living in enchantment; should she get the tallow of each ox by itself and entire, she would bring back the three brothers to life, and they would destroy all the Fenians of Erin. We will hang up the tallow in the smoke of the Black-Blue Giant's chimney; it will lose some of itself there. When she gets it, it will not have full weight. We will change your beds and your tables while you are waiting, so as to observe the injunction. You must do this; for if you do not make an end of Grainne, Grainne will make an end of you.'

All was done as the forester said. At the end of a week, when Faolan and his friend were setting out for Erin, the giant and his wife fell to weeping and wailing after their daughter, who was going with Dyeermud.

'We will come back again soon,' said Dyeermud, 'and then will have a great feast for this marriage.'

'It is here that I will have my marriage feast, too,' said Faolan.

The forester, who was an old man, said perhaps he might have a marriage feast at that time as well as the others. At this they all laughed.

The giant and his wife were then satisfied; and the company set out for the forester's cabin. When they reached the cabin, the forester said to Dyeermud, 'As I served you, I hope that you will do me a good turn.'

'I will do you a good turn,' said Dyeermud, 'if I lose my life in doing it.'

'Cut off my head,' said the forester.

'I will not,' replied Dyeermud.

'Well,' said the old man, 'if you do not, you will leave me in great distress; for I, too, am under enchantment, and there is no power to save me unless you, Dyeermud, cut off my head with the sword that killed the oldest of the oxen.'

When Dyeermud saw how he could serve the forester, he cut off his head with one blow, and there rose up before him a young man of twenty-one years.

'My name is Arthur, son of Deara,' said the young man to Dyeermud; 'I was enchanted by my stepmother, and I am in love with your sister since I saw her two years ago on Ventry Strand, when you were in combat with the Champion of the Eastern World. Will you let your sister marry me?'

'I will,' replied Dyeermud; 'and she will not marry any man but the one that I will choose for her.'

'I helped Faolan,' said Arthur, 'in all his struggles, except that against the Dun Ox.'

Next day all went to the castle of the four champions and their sister, and, leaving the women in that place, they set out for Erin.

When the Fenians of Erin saw them sailing in toward Ventry Strand, they raised three shouts of joyous welcome. Whoever was glad, or was not glad, Grainne was glad, because there was an end, as she thought, to her suffering. Indeed, she would not have lived at all had she kept the injunctions, but she did not; she received meat and eggs on Sliav Iolar from all the women who took pity on her and went to visit her. So when she got the tallow, she weighed it, and finding it some ounces short, gave out three piercing wails of distress, and when Dyeermud, who was of fiery temper, saw that Faolan was not willing to punish the woman, he raised his own sword, and swept the head off her.

Fin embraced Faolan and welcomed him. Dyeermud went to his mother and sister.

'Will you marry a young champion whom I have brought with me?' asked he of the sister.

'I will marry no one,' said she, 'but the man you will choose for me.'

'Very well,' said Dyeermud, 'there is such a man outside.' He led her out, and she and Arthur were well pleased with each other.

Dyeermud, with his sister and Arthur and Faolan, set out on the following day, and never stopped nor stayed till they reached the castle of the four champions and their sister; and, taking Faolan's betrothed and Dyeermud along with them, they travelled on till they stopped at the castle of the Black-Blue Giant. Faolan's mother was there before him; and glad was she, and rejoiced, to see her own son.

There were three weddings in one at the castle of the giant: Arthur and Dyeermud's sister; Faolan and the sister of the four champions; Dyeermud and the daughter of the Black-Blue Giant.

When the feasting was over, Faolan's mother called him, and asked, 'Will you go to my kingdom, which is yours by inheritance, the country of the Dark Men, and rule there?'

'I will,' said Faolan, 'on condition that I am to be sent for if ever the Fenians should need my assistance.' He then gave his share in the land of the wild hag, and his claim to the castles of the Cat of Gray Fort, the Kitten of Cul MacKip, and the Dun Ox, to Arthur and Dyeermud, and these two shared those places between them. They attended Faolan and his wife to the country of the Dark Men, and then returned. Faolan's mother went to Fintra, and lived with Fin MacCool.

FIN MACCOOL, THE HARD GILLA, AND THE HIGH KING

On a day when the Fenians were living at Fintra, Fin MacCool called them together, held a council, complained of remissness, and warned the men to be cautious, to keep a better watch on the harbours, and to take good care of their arms. They promised to do better in future, and asked Fin to forgive them for that time. Fin forgave them, and sent men to keep watch on Cruach Varhin.

When on the mountain awhile, the chief sentry saw, in the distance, a man leading a horse toward Fintra. He thought to run down with word to Fin, but did not; he waited to see what kind of person was coming. The man leading the horse was far from being tidy: his shoes were untied, and the strings hanging down; on his shoulders was a mantle, flapping around in the wind. The horse had a broad, surly face; his neck was thick at the throat, and thin toward the body: the beast was scrawny, long-legged, lean, thin-maned, and ugly to look at. The only bridle on the horse was a long, heavy chain; the whip in the hand of the man was a strong iron staff. Each blow that the man gave his steed was heard through the glens and the mountains, and knocked echoes out of every cliff in that region. Each pull that the man gave the bridle was that strong, that you would think he'd tear the head off the ugly beast's body. Every clump of earth that the horse rooted up with his feet, in striving to hold back, was three times the size of a sod of turf ready for burning.

'It is time for me now,' said the watchman, at last, 'to hurry from this, and tell Fin,' and with that he rushed down from Cruach Varhin.

Fin saw him coming, and was ready for his story; and not too soon was it told; for just then the horseman came up to the King of the Fenians at Fintra.

'Who are you?' inquired Fin.

'I do not know who my father was,' said the stranger. 'I am of one place as well as another. Men call me the Hard Gilla; and it is a good name: for no matter how well people treat me I forget all they do. I have heard, though, that you give most wages, and best treatment of any man.'

'I will give you good wages,' said Fin, 'and fair treatment; but how much do you want of me?'

'I want whatever I ask.'

'I will give you that and more, if I promise,' said Fin.

'I am your man,' said the Gilla. 'Now that we have agreed, I may let my horse out to graze, I suppose?'

'You may,' answered Fin.

The Gilla untied the chain bridle from his horse, and struck him with the chain. The beast went to the other horses; but if he did, he fell to eating the mane, legs, ears, and tail of each one of them, and ate all till he came to a steed grazing apart, and this steed belonged to Conan Maol. Conan ran, caught the ugly old horse by the skull, and pulled him up to his owner.

'Mind your wicked old cripple!' cried Conan, in anger.

'If any man does not like how my horse feeds, he may herd the good steed himself.'

When Conan heard this insolence, he went to the adviser for counsel. The adviser told him to go upon the back of the horse, and to ride till he broke him. Conan mounted the horse; but not a stir could he get from the stubborn beast.

'He is used to heavy loads,' said the adviser. 'Let others mount with you.'

The Fenians were mounting the horse till twenty-eight men of them went up with Conan. The twenty-nine began then to wallop the horse, but could not raise a stir out of him. The old horse only cocked one ear.

FIN MACCOOL, THE HARD GILLA, AND THE HIGH KING

When the Gilla saw the twenty-nine on his horse, he called out, 'It seems that we do not agree; and the sooner I go from this place the better.'

He tightened his cloak, flapping loose on his body, tied his shoes, and said, 'In place of praising, I will dispraise you.' Then he went in front of the horse. The horse raised his tail and his head, and between his tail and his neck he held the men firmly. Some tried to jump off, but were as secure on the horse as his own skin. Conan was the first to speak. When he saw that he could not spring from the horse, he turned to Fin, and cried out, 'I bind you, O Fin, not to eat two meals off the one table, or sleep two nights on the one bed, till you have me freed from this serpent.'

When Fin and the Fenians heard this, they looked at one another. The adviser spoke then, and said, 'There is no time for delay. We have here a man to follow, and he is Leeagawn of Lúachar Garv.'

Fin called Leeagawn, and he went after the steed quickly, caught him at the edge of the strand, and seized him by the tail; but if he did, he grew fast to the tail of the horse, and was pulled forward to the strand. He tried to loose himself from the tail, but no use for him to try. The horse drew him into the water. The sea opened before the strange steed, and closed behind. The Gilla ran in front. Twenty-nine men were on the back of the horse, and one fixed to his tail.

Fin and the Fenians were greatly distressed at the sight, but could give no assistance. They held council; and the druid said, 'There is an old ship in Ben Eadan; put that ship in repair, and sail after the steed.'

'Let us go,' said the Fenians, 'for the ship.'

As they were making ready to start, two young champions hurried up to Fin, and saluted him.

'Who are ye?' asked Fin, returning the salute; 'and whither are ye going?'

'We are the two sons of a king,' replied they; 'each has a gift, and we have come to you to know which is the better gift to live by. The two gifts are two powers left us by our father.'

'What is your power?' asked Fin of the elder brother.

'Do you see this branch?' said he. 'If I strike the water of the harbour with this branch, the harbour will be filled with ships till they are crushing one another. When you choose the one you like, I will make the others disappear as quickly as you can bow your head.'

'What can you do?' asked Fin of the younger brother.

'If a wild duck were to dart forth from her nest, I could keep in sight of the bird, and she going straight or crooked, high or low, I could catch her before she could fly back to the nest from which she came.'

When they had done speaking, Fin said, 'I have never been in more need of your help than I am at this moment.' He told them then of the Gilla, and of all that had happened. The elder brother struck the harbour with his branch; the harbour was filled with ships in one minute. Fin chose the ship he liked best, and said, 'I'll take that one.' In a twinkle the other ships vanished.

When the men were all ready to go on the ship, Fin called Oisin, and said to him, 'I leave the ruling of Erin with you, till I come back to this harbour.' He bade farewell then to Oisin and the Fenians. The younger of the two champions stood at the prow, the elder at the stern. The younger followed the horse in crooked and straight paths through the sea, told his brother how to steer on the voyage. They kept on till, at length, and at last, they came to a haven with a steep, rugged shore, and no ship could enter.

'This is where the steed went in,' said the younger brother.

When the Fenians saw the haven, they looked at one another. It was a very steep place; and all said, 'We cannot land here.'

'There will be an evil report for the Fenians of Erin, or for men trained by Fin, if no one can spring to land,' said the druid.

'Well,' said Dyeermud, 'there was never a man at Fintra who could make such a spring, if I cannot make it.'

He buckled his belt firmly, and went to the stern of the ship to find space for a run; then he rushed to the prow, and rose with one bound to the top of the cliff. When he looked back, and saw his comrades below, he was frightened.

Dyeermud left the ship and the Fenians, and walked forward alone. Toward evening, he saw a herd of deer; he pursued them, and caught a doe, which he killed; he made a fire, roasted the carcass, ate of it, and drank pure spring water. He made a hut then of limbs, and slept quietly till morning. After breakfast, a gruagach came the way, and called out to him, 'Is not Erin wide enough for you to live in, instead of coming hither to steal my herds from me?'

'Though I might have been willing to go when you came,' replied Dyeermud, 'I will not go now since you speak so unmannerly.'

'You must fight with me then,' said the gruagach.

'I will indeed,' said Dyeermud.

They took their spears and swords, and fought all that day until evening, when the gruagach saw that Dyeermud was getting the upper hand. He leaped into the spring from which Dyeermud had drunk the cool water. Dyeermud ran quickly, and thrust his sword into the water, but no sign of the gruagach.

'I will watch for you to-morrow,' said Dyeermud to himself; so he waited near the spring until morning.

The gruagach stood before him next day more threatening to look at than ever, and said, 'It seems you hadn't fighting enough from me yesterday.'

'I told you that I would not go,' answered Dyeermud, 'till I had knocked satisfaction out of you for your ugly speech.'

They went at each other then, and fought fiercely till very near evening. Dyeermud watched the spring closely, and when the gruagach leaped in, he was with him. In the side of the spring was a passage; the two walked through that passage, and came out in a kingdom where there was a grand castle, and seven men at each side of the door. When Dyeermud went toward the castle, the fourteen rushed against him. He slew these, and all others who faced him till nightfall. He would not enter the castle, but stretched himself on the ground, and fell fast asleep. Soon a champion came, tapped him lightly with a sword, and said, 'Rise now, and speak to me.'

Dyeermud sprang up, and grasped his sword.

'I am not an enemy, but a friend,' said the champion. 'It is not proper for you to be sleeping in the midst of your enemies. Come to my castle; I will entertain you, and give you good keeping.'

Dyeermud went with the stranger; and they became faithful friends. 'The king of this country, which is called Tir Fohin [Land Under the

Wave], is my brother,' said the champion. 'The kingdom is rightfully mine, and 'tis I that should be King of Tir Fohin; but my brother corrupted my warriors with promises, so that all except thirty men of them left me.'

This champion was called the Knight of Valour. Dyeermud told this knight his whole story, – told of the Hard Gilla, and his long-legged, scrawny, thin-maned, ugly old horse.

'I am the man,' said the knight, 'that will find out the Hard Gilla for you. That Gilla is the best swordsman and champion in this land, and the greatest enchanter. Your men, brought away by him, are as safe and as sound as when they left Erin. He is a good friend of mine.'

'Now,' said Dyeermud, 'for your kindness (you might have killed me when I was asleep), and for your entertainment, I give my word to fight against your brother, and win back your kingdom.'

Dyeermud sent a challenge to the King of Tir Fohin. The knight and Dyeermud, with the knight's thirty men, fought against the king's forces, fought all that day until evening; then the king withdrew to the castle to keep his hold firm on the chief place, but Dyeermud rushed in, brought him out to the green, threw him on the flat of his back, and shouted, 'Are you not satisfied yet?'

'I am if the men are,' said the king.

'Will you obey the Knight of Valour?' asked Dyeermud of the men.

'We will,' answered they.

The men gave their word to obey with all faithfulness. Dyeermud gave the false king thirty men then; and the Knight of Valour became king in his own land. On the morrow, Dyeermud and the king went with forces to the Gilla's castle; and when they entered the gates, the Gilla came out, received them with welcome and hand-shaking. There was great rejoicing, and good cheer at the Gilla's castle.

When Dyeermud did not return to the vessel, Fin and the two young champions thought to find an easier landing in some place; they put their ship around, and sailed forward, sailed and sailed; and where should they come at last but to the castle of the King of Sorách (Light), who received them with welcome, and entertained them with the best that he had in his castle.

FIN MACCOOL, THE HARD GILLA, AND THE HIGH KING

But they were hardly seated at table, when the chief messenger of the King of Sorách came hurrying in and said, that there was a fleet sailing toward them, which was as numerous as the sands on the seashore, that it was coming for tribute, which had not been collected for many a year.

The king had a grieved and sorrowful face. 'That is the High King of the World coming against me,' said he.

'Never fear,' said Fin MacCool. 'Cheer up, and have courage. I and my men will stand up for you. We will fight to the death to defend you.'

On the following day, the High King sent forces to land, to attack the King of Sorách in his castle. These forces were under command of Borb Sinnsior na Gah, son of the High King. The greatest delight of the High King was his daughter, a beautiful maiden called Teasa Taov Geal; and the thought came to her that day to see the battle. 'I will go,' said she, 'with my brother, and see him take the king's castle.'

On Fin's side, the two young champions his guides were eager to be in the struggle; but Fin would not hear of that. 'You must stay with the ship,' said he, 'and take us to Erin, when the time comes.'

As soon as Fin saw the attack was led by the son of the High King, he said, 'I will take command in the battle, and lead the men in action to-day. We will show the invaders what the Fenians do in battle.'

Oscar went with Fin, and so did Goll MacMorna. The battle raged grandly; the men of the High King fell in crowds until evening, what was left of them then went to the ships, and sailed back in haste to their master.

When the news reached the High King, he called his druid for advice.

'This is not the time to make war on the King of Sorách,' said the druid; 'for Fin MacCool and his men are living in friendship at his castle; they will help him to the end of this struggle. Go home for the present, and come again when Fin has gone back to Erin.'

The king was inclined to do this; but his daughter had seen Fin MacCool in the battle, and fallen in love with him. She sent him a message, saying, 'I will go with you. I will leave my father for your sake. I love you.'

The answer that Fin sent, was to come to him; he would take her with gladness to Erin.

The king was grieved at the loss of his daughter. 'I might go home now,' said he, 'and come back at another time; but how can I go, and leave my daughter behind me?'

There was a champion called Lavran MacSuain, who could steal anything while men were asleep, and make them sleep all the more, but could not do harm to them. Lavran volunteered to bring back the daughter.

'If I find them asleep,' said he, 'I will bring her back; if you give me a reward.'

'I will pay you well,' said the king. 'I will not spare rewards on you, if you bring me my daughter.'

When Lavran came to where Fin was, he found him and the Fenians asleep, and put them in a still deeper sleep. He brought Teasa Taov Geal to her father's ship then. The fleet sailed away in the night; and at daybreak there was not a trace of it.

Next morning when Fin woke, and found that the king's daughter was gone, he sprang up, and was raging with anger. He sent men to look for the feet; but not a boat nor a ship was in sight.

Oscar and Goll, seeing Fin in such passion, said, 'We will go, if a druid goes with us. He will find out the castle by his knowledge; and we will bring the woman back, or die while striving to bring her.'

Next morning, Goll and Oscar took a ready ship from the fleet of the King of Sorách, set sail, and never stopped till they touched land near the castle of the High King.

'The best way for us,' said the druid, on landing, 'is to say that we are bards, till we learn where the strength of the king is.'

'We will not do that,' said Oscar. 'We will go straight forward, and bring the woman back with the strength of our arms.'

They went straight from the strand toward the castle. At the wayside was a rath where the daughter of the king was at that time, and no great number of men there to guard her. Goll and Oscar attacked the guards, cut them down, and took Taov Geal.

'The king is coming home from a hunt,' said the druid; 'it is better to hurry back to our ship.'

FIN MACCOOL, THE HARD GILLA, AND THE HIGH KING

'We will sharpen our weapons,' said Oscar, 'and strike the king's men, if they come toward us; but do you take the woman, and go in all haste to the ship. We will stay behind to protect you.'

The druid took Taov Geal, who was willing and glad, when she heard who had come for her. They reached the ship safely. Goll and Oscar came soon after, sprang into the ship, set sail, and never stopped till they brought Teasa Taov Geal to Fin at the castle of the King of Sorách. There was a feast then far greater than the one which the High King had interrupted the first day.

'I will take you to Erin,' said Fin to Taov Geal.

'I will go with you,' said she.

'I know the Hard Gilla well,' said the King of Sorách to Fin MacCool. 'I will go with you to him; he is a great champion, and a mighty enchanter.'

The king and his men, with Fin and the Fenians, went to the lands of the Gilla; and when he saw them all, he brought them into his castle, and treated them well. Dyeermud and the King of Tir Fohin were there also; they had been enjoying themselves, and feasting with the Gilla, while Fin and the others were fighting with the High King, and stealing his daughter.

Conan and the twenty-nine Fenians were all in good health; and Fin had the daughter of the High King in the castle, intending to take her to Erin.

Said Fin to the Gilla one day, 'It was you and Conan who had the first quarrel, he and you are the men who began these adventures. I will leave him and you to end the whole story. Conan is not easy to talk with, and you are a hard man to conquer.'

Conan was called up.

'What have you to say of our host,' inquired Fin; 'and what would you do for him?'

'I was treated here as well as you have ever treated me in Fintra, or as any man treated me in another place,' said Conan. 'My sentence is this, Let him come to Erin with us in our ship, feast with us in Fintra, and ride home on his own horse.'

'I will do that,' said the Gilla.

Conan and the Gilla, with all the Fenians, went to the ship. Fin brought the daughter of the High King on board, and all sailed away to Erin.

The Gilla was entertained to his heart's content, till one day he said, 'I must leave you now, and go to my own place.'

Conan and a number of Fenians went to the seashore to see him ride away. 'Where is your horse?' asked Conan.

'Here,' said the Gilla.

Conan turned to see the ugly long-legged beast, but saw nothing. He turned then to look at the Gilla, but saw only mist stretching out toward the water.

THE BATTLE OF VENTRY

It was predicted seven years before the battle of Ventry, that Daire Donn, High King of the Great World, would invade Erin to conquer it. Fin MacCool, for this reason, placed sentries at the chief ports of Erin. At Ventry, Conn Crithir was stationed on the top of Cruach Varhin to give warning; but he overslept when the fleet came: and the first news he had of its coming was from the cries of people attacked by the invaders. Conn Crithir sprang up, and said, –

'Great is the misery that has come by my sleep; but Fin and the Fenians will not see me alive after this. I will rush into the midst of the foreigners; and they will fall by me, till I fall by them.'

So he ran down toward the strand. On the way, he saw three strange women running before him. He increased his speed; but, unable to overtake them, he caught his spear to hurl it at the one nearest him.

The women stopped that moment, and cried, 'Stay your hand, and do not kill innocent women who have come not to harm but to help you.'

'Who are ye?' asked Conn Crithir.

'We are three sisters who have come from Tirnanog. We are all three in love with you; but no one of us is jealous of the other. We will hide you with an enchanted cloud, so that you can attack the foreign forces unseen. We have a well of healing at the foot of Sliav Iolar; and its waters will cure every wound made in battle. After bathing in it, you will be as sound as the day you were born.'

Conn Crithir was grateful, and hurried to the strand, where he slew four hundred men of the enemy on the first day. He was covered with wounds himself; but the three sisters took him to the well. He bathed in it, and was as sound as on the day he was born.

Conn Crithir was this way in struggle and combat, till Teastalac Treunmhar, the chief courier of Fin MacCool, came to Ventry.

'Have you tidings of Fin and the Fenians?' asked Conn.

'I have. They are at the River Lee,' said Teastalach.

'Go to them quickly,' said Conn, 'and tell how we are here. Let them come hither to save us.'

'It would ill become me to go till I had moistened my sword in the blood of the enemy,' said Teastalach; and he sent a challenge for single combat to the High King.

'I am the man to meet that warrior,' said Colahan MacDochar, the king's champion; and he went on shore without waiting.

Colahan was thirty feet in height, and fifteen around the waist. When he landed, he went at Teastalach. They fought one hour, and fought with such fury, the two of them, that their swords and spears went to pieces. The sword of Colahan was broken at the hilt; but of Teastalach's blade there remained a piece as long as the breadth of a man's palm.

Colahan, who was enraged that any champion could stand against him for the space of even one hour, seized Teastalach in his arms, to carry him living to the ship of the High King, twist off his head there, and raise it on a stake before the forces of the world. When he came to deep water, he raised Teastalach on his shoulder; but Teastalach, the swift courier of Fin MacCool, turned quickly, cut the head off his enemy, brought that head to the strand, and made boast of his deed.

Now Teastalach went to where Fin and his forces were, and told him of all that happened. Fin marched straightway, and never stopped nor rested till he came to Maminch, within twenty miles of Ventry. Fin rested there for the night; but Oscar, son of Oisin, with Conn Ceadach and one other, went forward. Before going, Oscar turned to Fin, and said, 'Chew your thumb, and tell us what will be the end of our struggle.'

Fin chewed his thumb from the skin to the flesh, from the flesh to the bone, from the bone to the marrow, from the marrow to the juice, and said, 'The victory will be on our side, but little else will be with us. The battle will last for a day and a year, and every day will be a day of fierce struggle. No man of the foreigners will escape; and on our side few will be left living, and none without wounds.'

Oscar went his way then till he reached Ventry. Fin came on the second day, and stopped with all his forces at Rahonáin. Next morning, he asked, 'Who will command the battle to-day?'

'We will go with two hundred,' said Oisin and Oscar.

They went toward the harbour; and a great troop landed to meet them. The two parties faced each other then, and fought till near evening; when all were killed on the side of the foreigners except three smiths, and of Fin's men there remained only Oisin, Oscar, and Goll, son of Morna.

On the following morning, Oisin and Oscar went with two hundred more, but without Goll. The foreign troop came in numbers as before: and at midday there was no man left living of Fin's men but Oisin and Oscar; on the foreign side all had fallen except the three smiths, who were mighty champions. Oscar and Oisin faced the smiths. Oscar had two men against him; and Oisin's enemy was forcing him backward toward the water. Fin, seeing this, feared for his son, and sent a poet to praise and encourage him.

'Now is the time to prove your valour and greatness, Oisin,' said the poet. 'You never went to any place but a king's daughter, or a high beauty, fell in love with you. Many are looking this day at you; and now is your time to show bravery.'

Oisin was greatly encouraged; so he grew in fury and increased on his blows, till at last he swept the head off his enemy. About the same time, Oscar killed the two other smiths; but, being faint from open wounds and blood-loss, he fell senseless on the strand. Oisin, his father, rushed to him, and held him till aid came. They carried him to Rahonáin, where, after a long time, he revived.

The smiths had one brother in the fleet of the High King, and his name was Dealv Dura. This man, who was the first champion in the armies of the High King, fell into great grief, and swore to have vengeance for his brothers. He went to the High King, and said, 'I will go alone to the strand, and will slay two hundred men every day till I have slain all the forces of Erin; and if any man of your troops interfere, I will kill him.'

Next morning, Fin asked who would conduct the battle on that day.

'I will,' said Duvan, son of Donn, 'with two hundred men.'

'Go not,' said Fin. 'Let another go.'

But Duvan went to the strand with two hundred; and there was no one before him but Dealv Dura, who demanded two hundred men in combat. A shout of derision went up from Duvan's men; but Dealv rushed at them, and he slew the two hundred without a man of them being able to put a sword-cut on him. Then, taking a hurley and ball, Dealv Dura threw up the ball, and kept it in the air with the hurley from the western to the eastern end of the strand, without letting it touch the ground even one time. Then, he put the ball on his right foot, and kicked it high in the air; when it was near the earth, he sent it up with the left foot, and kept the ball in the air with his two feet, and never let it touch the earth once, while he was rushing from one end of the strand to the other. Next, he put the ball on his right knee, sent it up with that, caught it on the left knee, and kept the ball in the air with his two knees while he was running from one end of the strand to the other. Last, he put the ball on one shoulder, threw it up with that shoulder, caught it on the other, and kept the ball in the air with his two shoulders while he was rushing like a blast of March wind from one end of the strand to the other.

When he had finished, he walked back and forth on the strand vauntingly, and challenged the men of Erin to do the like of those feats.

Next day, Fin sent out two hundred men. Dealv Dura was down on the strand before them, and not a man of the two hundred returned.

Day after day, two hundred went out, and all fell before Dealv Dura. A report ran now through all Erin that Fin's troops were perishing daily from one man; and this report reached at last the castle of the King of Ulster. The king had one son, and he only thirteen years of age. This son, who was the fairest and shapeliest youth in Erin, said to his father, 'Let me go to help Fin MacCool and his men.'

'You are not old enough, nor strong enough, my son; your bones are too soft.'

THE BATTLE OF VENTRY

When the youth insisted, his father confined him, and set twelve youths, his own foster-brothers, to guard him, lest he might escape to Ventry Strand.

The king's son was enraged at being confined, and said to his foster-brothers, 'It is through valour and daring that my father gained glory in his young years; and why should I not win a name as well as he? Help me, and I will be a friend to you forever.'

He talked and persuaded, till they agreed to go with him to Fin MacCool. They took arms then, hurried across Erin, and, when they came to Ventry, Dealv Dura was on the strand reviling the Fenians.

'O Fenians of Erin,' said Oisin, 'many have fallen by Dealv Dura; and I would rather die in combat against him, than see the ruin he brings every day!'

A great cry was raised by all at these words.

Now the son of the King of Ulster stood before Fin, and saluted him.

'Who are you?' asked Fin.

'I am Goll, son of the King of Ulster, and these twelve are my foster-brothers. We have come to give you what assistance we can.'

'My welcome to you,' said Fin.

The reviling of Dealv Dura was heard now again.

'Who is that?' asked the king's son from Ulster.

'An enemy asking for two hundred warriors of mine to meet him,' said Fin.

Here the twelve foster-brothers went to the strand, unknown to the king's son.

'You are not a man,' said Conan Maol, 'and none of these twelve could face any warrior.'

'I have never seen the Fenians till this day,' said the king's son, 'still I know that you are Conan Maol, who never speaks well of any man; but you will see that I am not in dread of Dealv Dura, or any champion on earth. I will go down now, and meet the warrior single-handed.'

Fin and the Fenians stopped the young hero, and detained him, and talked to him. Then, Conan began again, and said, 'In six days that champion has slain twelve hundred men; and there was not a man of the twelve hundred who could not have killed twelve hundred like you every day.'

These words enraged the king's son. He sprang up, and then heard the shouting of Dealv Dura on the strand. 'What does he want now?' asked the king's son.

'More men for combat,' said Conan. 'He has just slain your twelve body-guards.'

With that the king's son seized his weapons, and no man could stop or delay him. He rushed to the strand, and went toward Dealv Dura. When the champion saw the youth coming, he sneered, and the hosts of the High King sent up a roar of laughter; for they thought Fin's men were all killed, since he had sent a stripling to meet Dealv Dura. The courage of the boy was all the greater from the derision; and he rushed on Dealv Dura, who got many wounds from the youth before he knew it.

They fought a sharp, bloody combat; and no matter how the champion, Dealv Dura, used his strength, swiftness, and skill, he was met by the king's son: and if the world could be searched, from its eastern edge to its western border, no braver battle would be found than was that one.

The two fought through the day, the hosts of the Great World and the Fenians cheering and urging them on. Toward evening their shields were hacked to pieces, and their weapons all shivered, but they did not stop the battle; they grappled and caught each other, and fought so that the sand on the beach was boiling like water beneath them. They wrestled that way, seeing nothing in the world but each other, till the tide of the sea went over them, and drowned the two there before the eyes of the Fenians and the hosts of the High King.

A great cry of wailing and sorrow was raised on both sides, when the water closed over the champions. Next morning, after the tide-ebb, the two bodies were found stiff and cold, each one in the grasp of the other; but Dealv Dura was under the king's son, so it was known that the youth was a better man than the other.

The king's son was buried with great honour by the Fenians; and never before did they mourn for a hero as on that day.

THE BATTLE OF VENTRY

'Who will command the battle this time?' asked Fin, on the following morning.

'I and my son Oscar,' said Oisin.

They went to the strand with two hundred men; and against them came the King of France with his forces. The two sides fought with such venom that at midday there was no one alive on either side but Oscar, Oisin, and the King of France. The king and Oisin were fighting at the eastern end of Ventry; and the king gave such a blow that he knocked a groan from Oisin. Oscar, who was at the western end of the strand then, – Oscar, of noble deeds, the man with a heart that never knew fear, and a foot that never stepped back before many or few, – rushed to see who had injured his father; and the noise that he made was like the noise of fifty horses while racing.

The king looked toward the point where the thundering sound was, and saw Oscar coming. He knew then that unless he escaped he had not long to live; his beauty and bravery left him, and his terror was like that of a hundred horses at the sound of a thunderbolt. Lightness of mind and body came on him; he stretched himself, sprang up, flew through the air, and never stopped till he came down in Glean nan Allt, – a place to which, since that time, insane persons go, and every madman in Erin would go there in twenty four hours, if people would let him.

In the battle of the next day, the King of Norway was chief; and there was never such destruction of men in Erin before as on that day. This king had a venomous shield with red flames, and if it were put under the sea not one of its flames would stop blazing, and the king himself was not hotter from any of them. When he had the shield on his arm no man could come near him; and he went against the Fenians with only a sword. Not to use weapon had he come, but to let the poison of his shield fly among them. The balls of fire that he sent from the shield went through the bodies of men, so that each blazed up like a splinter of oak which had hung a whole year in the smoke of a chimney, and whoever touched the burning man, blazed up as well as he; and small was every evil that came into Erin before, when compared with that evil.

'Lift up your hands,' said Fin, 'and give three shouts of blessing to the man who will put some delay on that foreigner.'

CELTIC WARRIORS AND GIANTS

A smile came on the king's face when he heard the shouts that Fin's men were giving. It was then that the Chief of the Fenians of Ulster came near; and he had a venomous spear, the Crodearg. He looked at the King of Norway, and saw nothing of him without armor, save his mouth, and that open wide in laughter at the Fenians. He made a cast of his venomous spear, which entered the king's mouth, and went out through his neck. The shield fell, and its blazing was quenched with the life of its master. The chief cut the head off the king, and made boast of the deed; and his help was the best that the Fenians received from any man of their own men. Many were the deeds of that day; and but few of the forces of the High King went back to their ships in the evening.

On the following day, the foreigners came in thousands; for the High King had resolved to put an end to the struggle. Conan Maol, who never spoke well of any man, had a power which he knew not himself, and which no one in Erin knew except Fin. When Conan looked through his fingers at any man, that man fell dead the next instant.

Fin never told Conan of this, and never told any one; for he knew that Conan would kill all the Fenians when he got vexed if he knew his own power. When the foreigners landed, Fin sent a party of men with Conan to a suitable place, so that when the enemy were attacking, these men would look with Conan through their fingers at the enemy, and pray for assistance against them.

When Conan and his men looked through their fingers, the enemy fell dead in great numbers, and no one knew that it was Conan's look alone, without prayers or assistance from others, that slew them.

Conan and his company stood there all day, looking through their fingers and praying, whenever a new face made its way from the harbour.

The struggle lasted day after day, till his men spoke to the High King and said to him, 'We can never conquer unless you meet Fin in single combat.'

The king challenged Fin to meet him on the third day. Fin accepted, though he was greatly in dread; for he knew that the trunk of the

THE BATTLE OF VENTRY

High King's body was formed of one bone, and that no sword in the world could cut it but the king's own sword, which was kept in the Eastern World by his grandsire, the King of the Land of the White Men. That old king had seven chambers in a part of his castle, one inside the other. On the door of the outer chamber was one lock, on the second two, and so on to the door of the seventh and innermost chamber, which had seven locks, and in that chamber the sword and shield of the High King were kept. In the service of Daire Donn was a champion, a great wizard, who wished ill to the High King. This man went to Fin, and said, 'I will bring you the sword and shield from the Eastern World.'

'Good will be my reward to you,' said Fin, 'if you bring them in time.'

Away went the man in a cloud of enchantment, and soon stood before the old king. 'Your grandson,' said he, 'is to fight with Fin MacCool, and has sent me for his weapons.'

The old king had the sword and shield brought quickly, and gave them. The man hurried back to Erin, and gave the weapons to Fin on the eve of the battle.

Next morning, the High King came to the strand full of confidence. Believing himself safe, he thought he could kill Fin MacCool easily; but when he stood in front of the chief of the Fenians, and saw his own venomous sword unsheathed in the hand of his enemy, and knew that death was fated him from that blade, his face left him for a moment, and his fingers were unsteady.

He rallied, and thinking to win by surprise, rushed suddenly, fiercely and mightily, to combat. One of Fin's men sprang out, and dealt a great blow with a broadaxe; it laid open the helmet, cut some of the hair of the High King, but touched not the skin of his body. The High King with one blow made two parts of the Fenian, and, rushing at Fin, cut a slice from his shield, and a strip of flesh from his thigh. Fin gave one blow then in answer, which made two equal parts of the king, so that one eye, one ear, one arm, and one leg of him dropped on one side, and the other eye, ear, arm, and leg went to the other side.

Now, the hosts of the High King, and the Fenians of Erin, fought till there was no man standing in the field except one. He raised the body of the High King, and said, 'It was bad for us, O Fenians of Erin, but worse for you; I go home in health, and ye have fallen side by side. I will come again soon, and take all Erin.'

'Sad am I,' said Fin, as he lay on the field, 'that I did not find death before I heard these words from the mouth of a foreigner, and he going into the Great World with tidings. Is there any man alive near me?'

'I am,' said Fergus Finbel; 'and there is no warrior who is not lying in his blood save the chief man of the High King and your own foster-son, Caol.'

'Go to seek my foster-son,' said Fin.

Fergus went to Caol, and asked him how his health was. 'If my battle-harness were loosened, my body would fall asunder from wounds; but more grieved am I at the escape of the foreigner with tidings than at my own woful state. Take me to the sea, Fergus, that I may swim after the foreigner; perhaps he will fall by this hand before the life leaves me.'

Fergus took him to the sea; and he swam to the ship. The foreigner thought him one of his own men, and reached down to raise him to the ship-board; but Caol grasped the man firmly and drew him to the water. Both sank in the clear, cold sea, and were drowned.

No man saw the foreigner afterward; but Caol's body was carried by the waves, borne northward, and past the islands, till it came to land, at the port which is now called Caoil Cuan (Caol's Harbour).

NOTES

1 Lir was the sea-god, the Oceanns of the Celt; no doubt the same as the British Lear, the wild, white-headed old king, who had such singular daughters; two, monsters of cruelty, and one, exquisitely sweet, kind, and serene, viz.: Storm, Hurricane, and Calm.

2 This was the god Lu Lam-fada, i.e., Lu, the Long-Handed. The rainbow was his sling. Remember that the rod sling, familiar enough now to Irish boys, was the weapon of the ancient Irish, and not the sling which is made of two cords.

3 There were three war goddesses: – (1) Badb (pronounced Byve); (2) Macha, already referred to; (3) The Mor-Rigu or Mor-Reega, who was the greatest of the three.

4 This was Fergus Mac Leda, Fergus, son of Leda, one of the more ancient kings of Ulster. His contest with the sea-monster is the theme of a heroic tale.]

5 One of Ireland's many names.

6 This was the king already referred to who slew the sea-monster. The monster had left upon him that mark and memorial of the struggle.

7 High Druid, or Chief Druid. Similarly we have Ard-Ri or High King.

8 Macha's celebrated grey war-steed. The meaning of the allusion will be understood presently.

9 These were the gods of the pagan Irish. Tuatha=nations, De=gods,

Danan=of Dana. So it means the god nations sprung from Dana also called Ana. She is referred to in an ancient Irish Dictionary as *Mater deorum Hibernensium.*

10   Craftsman.

11   A bright yellow bronze, the secret of making which is now lost. The metal may be seen in our museums. In beauty it is superior to gold.

12   Conall the Victorious. He came second to Cuculain amongst the Red Branch Knights. He is the theme of many heroic stories. Once in a duel he broke the right arm of his opponent. He bade his seconds tie up his own corresponding arm.

13   Now the barony of Cooley, a mountainous promontory which the County of Louth projects into the Irish Sea.

14   A poetic spell or incantation. So even the Christian hymn of St. Patrick was called the lorica or breastplate of Patrick.

15   Ulla is the Gaelic root of Ulster.

16   Dethcaen is compounded of two words which mean respectively, colour, and slender.

17   Ges was the Irish equivalent of the *tabu.*

18   Now Dundalk, capital of the County of Louth.

19   The Irish Sea or St. George's Channel. Muirnict means the Ictian Sea.

20   A territory conterminous with the modern County of Louth

21   Now the Fews mountain lying on the direct way between Dundalk

NOTES

and Armagh.

22 Ath-a-cliah, i.e., the Ford of the Hurdles. It was the Irish name for Dublin.

23 Lu the Long-Handed son of Ethlenn. This mysterious being, being one of the deities of the pagan Irish, seems to have been the Sun-god.

24 This man was Mananan son of Lir. He was the Sea-god.

25 The goddess Macha, already referred to, had a horse which was called the Grey of Macha – Liath-Macha. He was said to be still alive dwelling invisibly in Erin.

26 The Gaelic word for mantle.

27 An ancient Milesian hero. Brogan was uncle of Milesius.

28 Now the Nanny-Water, a beautiful stream running from Tara to the sea.

29 The Ultonians were descended from Ir, son of Milesius.

30 Concobar's shield. When Concobar was in danger the shield roared. The sea, too, roared responsive.

31 One of the minor gods. He resembles Mars Sylvanus of the Romans to whom swine were sacrificed.

32 The queen of the infernal regions.

33 This was the demon referred to in the lines at the head of the chapter.

34 A four-cornered quadrangular cup.

35   A derivative from Grian, the sun. The grianan was an upper chamber, more elegantly furnished than the hall, usually with large windows and therefore well lit and reserved for the use of women.

36   Angus Ogue was the god of youth and beauty, son of the Dagda who seems to have been the genius of earth and its fertility or perhaps the Zeus of our Gaelic mythology.

37   The Shannon.

38   In scriptural language 'of the seed of the giants', huge, simple-hearted and simple-minded men, who could obey orders and ask no questions.

39   The Orkney Islands.

40   Badb, pronounced Byve, was primarily the scald-crow or carrion-crow, secondarily a Battle-Fury.

41   One of Ireland's ancient names.

42   The hound was the type of valour. Though Cuculain was pre-eminently the Hound, the Gaelic equivalents of this word will be discovered in most of the famous names of the cycle.

43   Angus Ogue's kisses became invisible birds whose singing inspired love.

44   The Albanagh were the people who inhabited the north and west of Scotland, in fact the Highlanders. In ancient times they and the Irish were regarded as one people.

45   The sea between Ireland and Scotland. 'Silent, O Moyle, be the roar of thy waters.'

NOTES

46   Mantle.

47   He was one of the sons of Fergus Mac Roy slain in the great civil war.

48   Terrible druidic obligations.

49   At Tailteen a man boasted that his wife could outrun Concobar's victorious chariot-steeds. Concobar compelled the woman to run against his horses. She won the race, but died at the goal leaving her curse upon the Red Branch.

50   This man was Lu the Long-Handed, the same who met him when he was leaving home.

51   A great sorceress who ruled the world under the earth.

52   This great deity resembled the Greek Phoebus Apollo. He led the rebellion of the gods against the Fomorian giants who had previously reduced them to a condition of intolerable slavery. Some say that he was Cuculain's true father. His favourite weapon was the sling, likened here to the rainbow. It was not a thong or cord sling, but a pliant rod such as boys in Ireland still make. The milky way was his chain.

53   On account of their descent from Ir, son of Milesius, the Red Branch were also called the Irians.

54   Mananan mac Lir, the sea-god.

55   Tec Brac or Speckled House, the armoury of the Ultonians.

56   This is the hight point, 'the size of a pig's back', which the sailor saw from the topmast.

57   Fin's wisdom came in each case from chewing his thumb, which

he pressed once on the Salmon of Knowledge. An account of this is given in a tale in my *Myths and Folk-Lore of Ireland*, p.211.